KT-364-929

Contents

Introduction

OUR NATIONAL HEALTH is Volume 323 in the **ISSUES** series. The aim of the series is to offer current, diverse information about important issues in our world, from a UK perspective.

ABOUT TITLE

Now, more than ever, the NHS as an institution is a hotly debated topic. With challenges such as staffing shortages and budget cuts, speculation is rife as to what the future holds. This book explores all of those issues but also looks at the health of our nation, including our fitness levels and causes of death.

OUR SOURCES

Titles in the **ISSUES** series are designed to function as educational resource books, providing a balanced overview of a specific subject.

The information in our books is comprised of facts, articles and opinions from many different sources, including:

⇨ Newspaper reports and opinion pieces

⇨ Website factsheets

⇨ Magazine and journal articles

⇨ Statistics and surveys

⇨ Government reports

⇨ Literature from special interest groups.

A NOTE ON CRITICAL EVALUATION

Because the information reprinted here is from a number of different sources, readers should bear in mind the origin of the text and whether the source is likely to have a particular bias when presenting information (or when conducting their research). It is hoped that, as you read about the many aspects of the issues explored in this book, you will critically evaluate the information presented.

It is important that you decide whether you are being presented with facts or opinions. Does the writer give a biased or unbiased report? If an opinion is being expressed, do you agree with the writer? Is there potential bias to the 'facts' or statistics behind an article?

ASSIGNMENTS

In the back of this book, you will find a selection of assignments designed to help you engage with the articles you have been reading and to explore your own opinions. Some tasks will take longer than others and there is a mixture of design, writing and research-based activities that you can complete alone or in a group.

Useful weblinks

www.bma.org.uk

www.bsa.natcen.ac.uk

www.theconversation.com

www.cqc.org.uk

www.fullfact.org

www.theguardian.com

www.huffingtonpost.co.uk

www.imperial.ac.uk

www.kingsfund.org.uk

www.macmillan.org.uk

www.nhs.uk

www.ons.gov.uk

www.pressassociation.com

www.redcross.org.uk

www.telegraph.co.uk

www.yougov.co.uk

FURTHER RESEARCH

At the end of each article we have listed its source and a website that you can visit if you would like to conduct your own research. Please remember to critically evaluate any sources that you consult and consider whether the information you are viewing is accurate and unbiased.

Our National Health

Independence Educational Publishers

First published by Independence Educational Publishers

The Studio, High Green

Great Shelford

Cambridge CB22 5EG

England

ISBN-13: 978 1 86168 773 9

Printed in Great Britain

Zenith Print Group

About the National Health Service (NHS)

The NHS was launched in 1948

It was born out of a long-held ideal that good healthcare should be available to all, regardless of wealth – one of the NHS's core principles. With the exception of some charges, such as prescriptions, optical services and dental services, the NHS in England remains free at the point of use for all UK residents. This currently stands at more than 64.6 million people in the UK and 54.3 million people in England alone.

The NHS in England deals with over one million patients every 36 hours. It covers everything, including antenatal screening, routine screenings (such as the NHS Health Check), treatments for long-term conditions, transplants, emergency treatment and end-of-life care.

Responsibility for healthcare in Northern Ireland, Scotland and Wales is devolved to the Northern Ireland Assembly, the Scottish Government and the Welsh Assembly Government, respectively.

In 2014, the Commonwealth Fund declared that in comparison with the healthcare systems of ten other countries (Australia, Canada, France, Germany, The Netherlands, New Zealand, Norway, Sweden, Switzerland and the US), the NHS was the most impressive overall. The NHS was rated as the best system in terms of efficiency, effective care, safe care, coordinated care, patient-centred care and cost-related problems. It was also ranked second for equity.

Scale

The NHS employs more than 1.5 million people, putting it in the top five of the world's largest workforces, together with the US Department of Defence, McDonalds, Walmart and the Chinese People's Liberation Army.

The NHS in England is the biggest part of the system by far, catering to a population of 54.3 million and employing around 1.2 million people. Of those, the clinically qualified staff include 150,273 doctors, 40,584 general practitioners (GPs), 314,966 nurses and health visitors, 18,862 ambulance staff, and 111,127 hospital and community health service (HCHS) medical and dental staff.

The NHS in Scotland, Wales and Northern Ireland employs 161,415, 84,000 and 66,000 people, respectively.

Funding

Funding for the NHS comes directly from taxation. Since the NHS transformation in 2013, the NHS payment system has become underpinned by legislation. The Health and Social Care Act 2012 moves responsibility for pricing from the Department of Health, to a shared responsibility for NHS England and NHS Improvement. When the NHS was launched in 1948, it had a budget of £437 million (roughly £15 billion at today's value). For 2015/16, the overall NHS budget was around £116.4 billion. NHS England is managing £101.3 billion of this.

The NHS structure explained

The Secretary of State for Health

The Secretary of State has overall responsibility for the work of the Department of Health (DH). DH provides strategic leadership for public health, the NHS and social care in England.

The Department of Health

The DH is responsible for strategic leadership and funding for both health and social care in England. The DH is a ministerial department, supported by 23 agencies and public bodies. For detailed information, visit the DH website.

NHS England

NHS England is an independent body, at arm's length to the Government. Its main role is to set the priorities and direction of the NHS and to improve health and care outcomes for people in England. See NHS England's Five Year Forward View, which sets out the future vision for the NHS.

NHS England is the commissioner for primary care services such as GPs, pharmacists and dentists, including military health services and some specialised services.

As part of the NHS Five Year Forward View, primary care co-commissioning was introduced. An example of this is NHS England inviting clinical commissioning groups (CCGs) to take on an increased role in the commissioning of GP services. You can read more about co-commissioning and the benefits on NHS England's website.

NHS England manages around £100 billion of the overall NHS budget and ensures that organisations are spending the allocated funds effectively. Resources are allocated to CCGs.

Clinical commissioning groups

CCGs replaced primary care trusts (PCTs) on 1 April 2013. CCGs are clinically led statutory NHS bodies responsible for the planning and commissioning of healthcare services for their local area. CCG members include GPs and other clinicians, such as nurses and consultants. They are responsible for about 60% of the NHS budget, commission most secondary care services, and play a part in the commissioning of GP services. The secondary care services commissioned by CCGs are:

⇨ planned hospital care

⇨ rehabilitative care

⇨ urgent and emergency care

(including out-of-hours and NHS 111)

⇨ most community health services

⇨ mental health services and learning disability services.

CCGs can commission any service provider that meets NHS standards and costs. These can be NHS hospitals, social enterprises, charities or private sector providers. However, they must be assured of the quality of services they commission, taking into account both National Institute for Health and Care Excellence (NICE) guidelines and the Care Quality Commission's (CQC) data about service providers.

Both NHS England and CCGs have a duty to involve their patients, carers and the public in decisions about the services they commission.

Health and wellbeing boards

Health and wellbeing boards were established by local authorities to act as a forum for local commissioners across the NHS, social care, public health and other services. The boards intended to:

⇨ increase democratic input into strategic decisions about health and wellbeing services

⇨ strengthen working relationships between health and social care

⇨ encourage integrated commiss-ioning of health and social care services.

Public Health England (PHE)

PHE provides national leadership and expert services to support public health, and also works with local government and the NHS to respond to emergencies. PHE:

⇨ co-ordinates a national public health service and delivers some elements of this

⇨ builds an evidence base to support local public health services

⇨ supports the public to make healthier choices

⇨ provides leadership to the public health delivery system

⇨ supports the development of the public health workforce.

Vanguards

Vanguards were introduced in 2015 as part of the NHS Five Year Forward View.

The 50 chosen vanguards are tasked to develop new care models and potentially redesign the health and care system. It is envisaged that this could lead to better patient care, service access and a more simplified system. Find out more about vanguards on NHS England's website or download the document *New care models: Vanguards – developing a blueprint for the future of NHS and care services* (PDF, 1.51Mb) from the NHS website.

Regulation – safeguarding people's interests

Responsibility for regulating particular aspects of care is now shared across a number of different bodies, such as:

⇨ the CQC

⇨ NHS Improvement – an umbrella organisation that brings together Monitor, NHS Trust Development Authority, Patient Safety, the National Reporting and Learning System, the Advancing Change team and the Intensive Support Teams

⇨ individual professional regulatory bodies, such as the General Medical Council, Nursing and Midwifery Council, General Dental Council and the Health and Care Professions Council

⇨ other regulatory, audit and inspection bodies – some of which are related to healthcare and some specific to the NHS.

Principles and values that guide the NHS

The NHS was created out of the ideal that good healthcare should be available to all, regardless of wealth. When it was launched by the then minister of health, Aneurin Bevan, on 5 July 1948, it was based on three core principles:

⇨ that it meet the needs of everyone

⇨ that it be free at the point of delivery

⇨ that it be based on clinical need, not ability to pay.

These three principles have guided the development of the NHS over more than 60 years and remain at its core.

In March 2011, the Department of Health published the NHS Constitution. It sets out the guiding principles of the NHS and your rights as an NHS patient.

The seven key principles guide the NHS in all it does. They are underpinned by core NHS values which have been derived from extensive discussions with staff, patients and the public.

1. The NHS provides a comprehensive service available to all

This principle applies irrespective of gender, race, disability, age, sexual orientation, religion, belief, gender reassignment, pregnancy and maternity or marital or civil partnership status. The service is designed to diagnose, treat and improve both physical and mental health. It has a duty to each and every individual that it serves and must respect their human rights. At the same time, it has a wider social duty to promote equality through the services it provides and to pay particular attention to groups or sections of society where improvements in health and life expectancy are not keeping pace with the rest of the population.

2. Access to NHS services is based on clinical need, not an individual's ability to pay

NHS services are free of charge, except in limited circumstances sanctioned by Parliament.

3. The NHS aspires to the highest standards of excellence and professionalism

⇨ in the provision of high-quality care that is safe, effective and focused on patient experience

⇨ in the people it employs, and in the support, education, training and development they receive

⇨ in the leadership and management of its organisations

⇨ and through its commitment to innovation and to the promotion, conduct and use of research to improve the current and future health and care of the population.

Respect, dignity, compassion and care should be at the core of how patients and staff are treated – not only because that is the right thing to do, but because patient safety, experience and outcomes are all improved when staff are valued, empowered and supported.

4. The NHS aspires to put patients at the heart of everything it does

It should support individuals to promote and manage their own health. NHS services must reflect, and should be coordinated around and tailored to, the needs and preferences of patients, their families and their carers. Patients, with their families and carers where appropriate, will be involved in and consulted on all decisions about their care and treatment. The NHS will actively encourage feedback from the public, patients and staff, welcome it and use it to improve its services.

5. The NHS works across organisational boundaries and in partnership with other organisations in the interest of patients, local communities and the wider population.

The NHS is an integrated system of organisations and services bound together by the principles and values reflected in the Constitution. The NHS is committed to working jointly with other local authority services, other public sector organisations and a wide range of private and voluntary sector organisations to provide and deliver improvements in health and wellbeing.

6. The NHS is committed to providing best value for taxpayers' money and the most effective, fair and sustainable use of finite resources.

Public funds for healthcare will be devoted solely to the benefit of the people that the NHS serves.

7. The NHS is accountable to the public, communities and patients that it serves

The NHS is a national service funded through national taxation. The Government sets the framework for the NHS, and it is accountable to Parliament for its operation. However, most decisions in the NHS, especially those about the treatment of individuals and the detailed organisation of services, are rightly taken by the local NHS and by patients with their clinicians. The system of responsibility and accountability for taking decisions in the NHS should be transparent and clear to the public, patients and staff. The Government will ensure that there is always a clear and up-to-date statement of NHS accountability for this purpose.

NHS values

Patients, public and staff have helped develop this expression of values that inspire passion in the NHS, and that should underpin everything it does. Individual organisations will develop and build upon these values, tailoring them to their local needs. The NHS values provide common ground for cooperation to achieve shared aspirations, at all levels of the NHS.

Working together for patients

The value of "working together for patients" is a central tenet guiding service provision in the NHS and other organisations providing health services. Patients must come first in everything the NHS does. All parts of the NHS system should act and collaborate in the interests of patients, always putting patient interest before institutional interest, even when that involves admitting mistakes. As well as working with each other, health service organisations and providers should also involve staff, patients, carers and local communities to ensure they are providing services tailored to local needs.

Respect and dignity

Every individual who comes into contact with the NHS and organisations providing health services should always be treated with respect and dignity, regardless of whether they are a patient, carer or member of staff. This value seeks to ensure that organisations value and respect different needs, aspirations and priorities, and take them into account when designing and delivering services. The NHS aims to foster a spirit of candour and a culture of humility, openness and honesty, where staff communicate clearly and openly with patients, relatives and carers.

Commitment to quality of care

The NHS aspires to the highest standards of excellence and professionalism in the provision of high-quality care that is safe, effective and focused on patient experience. Quality should not be compromised – the relentless pursuit of safe, compassionate care for every person who uses and relies on services is a collective endeavour, requiring collective effort and collaboration at every level of the system. The delivery of high-quality care is dependent on feedback: organisations that welcome feedback from patients and staff are able to identify and drive areas for improvement.

Compassion

Compassionate care ties closely with respect and dignity in that individual patients, carers and relatives must be treated with sensitivity and kindness. The business of the NHS extends beyond providing clinical care and includes alleviating pain, distress, and making people feel valued and that their concerns are important.

Improving lives

The core function of the NHS is emphasised in this value – the NHS seeks to improve the health and wellbeing of patients, communities and its staff through professionalism, innovation and excellence in care. This value also recognises that to really improve lives the NHS needs to be helping people and their communities take responsibility for living healthier lives.

Everyone counts

We have a responsibility to maximise the benefits we obtain from NHS resources, ensuring they are distributed fairly to those most in need. Nobody should be discriminated or disadvantaged, and everyone should be treated with equal respect and importance.

Content reviewed April 2016

⇨ The above information is reprinted with kind permission from NHS Choices. Please visit www.nhs.uk for further information.

Which country has the world's best healthcare system?

We look at how patients pay for healthcare around the world and the general standard of care they might expect.

Healthcare is a costly item in national budgets, but who gets the best value for money, and who the best outcomes? We compare the systems in some of the world's leading countries for healthcare.

France

Upfront payments: yes

Data: France scores highly on GP numbers and on spending as a percentage of GDP, but it comes off badly in the Commonwealth Fund's international comparison reports, ranking only ninth out of 11 in the latest assessment.

Summary

Under France's state-run equivalent of the NHS, the majority of patients must pay the doctor or practitioner upfront. The state then reimburses them in part or in full. The patient has freedom to choose which doctor or service to visit.

All health transactions centre on a smartcard, the Carte Vitale. A GP visit costs €23 (£17), the Carte Vitale is swiped and the money is paid back into the patient's bank account within five days. In general, the state reimbursement rate is between 70% and 100%. The poorest people and the long-term sick are covered 100%.

Most people are signed up to a mutuelle, a semi-private insurance body, often related to their job, which tops up the remaining amount to be paid. If a patient is taken to the emergency department of a hospital, for example, they would provide their Carte Vitale, and depending on the health issue, could be reimbursed fully by the state. However, from November 2017 doctors such as GPs will have to waive the upfront fees for all patients, and instead the state and the mutuelle companies will pay doctors direct. At pharmacies, the patient pays upfront but swipes their Carte Vitale. A large number of prescribed medicines are reimbursed between 15% and 100%.

Ireland

Upfront payments: yes

Data: Ireland has more nurses than any other rich country, but its other metrics are distinctly average.

Summary

A GP visit in Ireland typically costs €40–€60. However, in 2015 the Irish government abolished charges for children under six while people with a medical card or GP visit card also receive free GP care.

In most cases, individuals pay for prescriptions from pharmacies capped at €144 per month under the Drugs Payment Scheme. Medical cardholders do not pay for medication but do pay a prescription charge of €2.50 per item (capped at €25 per month per person/family).

Patients are usually referred for secondary treatment by their GP unless they have entered the health system directly through an emergency department. Those attending emergency departments without being referred by a GP are charged €100 (with some exemptions). You are not charged if you are subsequently admitted as an inpatient but may be liable for hospital charges. The charge for an overnight stay in a public bed in a public hospital is €75 per day up to a maximum of €750 in 12 consecutive months.

As of the end of September, 46% of the population had health insurance, meaning they could be treated as a private patient in the public system or in a private hospital. Public patients who receive treatment in private hospitals pay for their own care.

Sweden

Upfront payments: yes

Data: Sweden is ranked third by the Commonwealth Fund, with a high proportion of doctors, above-average healthcare spending, and relatively low prescriptions of drugs.

Summary

Patients wishing to see a doctor pay a fee that varies depending on where they live, but usually about 100–200 kronor (£8-£16) for adults. Children pay only if they go to emergency rooms, about 120 kronor. For a visit to a specialist you pay up to 400 kronor and for emergency about 400 kronor. A hospital stay costs 100 kronor a day. You usually pay the same whether you choose a private or public clinic or hospital, as long as the private clinic is connected to the general healthcare system. And most are.

There is a limit to how much you pay for healthcare within a 12-month period. In most regions that is 1,100 kronor, but there are regions where the limit is just 900 kronor. Everything is free after that. Prescriptions are subsidised and you never pay more than 2,200 kronor in a 12-month period.

If you are referred to an expert, you pay a lower fee of about 100 kronor. If there are recurring visits you pay each time, but only up to 1,100 kronor within a 12-month period. Some regions charge small fees for the cost of an ambulance, about 150 kronor.

Only about 600,000 Swedes have a private health insurance – usually paid for by employers. It gives them the ability to skip the queue for procedures and operations, and to get to a doctor more quickly.

China

Upfront payments: yes, but low

Data: China scores poorly on just about every healthcare metric, apart from the growth in how much it spends each year on public health – a sign that it is trying to catch up.

Summary

Hundreds of millions of Chinese citizens lost the right to free public healthcare after the Communist party launched its economic reforms drive in the late 1970s.

Today, the cost of a hospital consultation is still relatively low. For those with blue government 'social insurance' cards, for example, a trip to Beijing's Friendship hospital can cost as little two yuan (20p). It costs about 100 yuan to be admitted to A&E while a night in a ward sets a patient back about the same.

But the often exorbitant cost of medicine and treatment can be enough to ruin a Chinese family.

Government officials say they hope to provide affordable healthcare to every Chinese citizen by 2020 and claim 95% of the population now boasts some kind of medical insurance. But in reality even those who do have insurance find it often fails to cover their bills.

Poorly paid doctors are notorious for overcharging patients for unnecessary prescriptions while even an ambulance ride to the hospital can set you back several hundred yuan.

Discontent over this state of affairs has made medicine a dangerous profession in China with a surge in verbal and physical attacks, including murders, against doctors in recent years.

US

Upfront payments: yes

Data: the US scores poorly on many fronts, ranked 11th out of 11 in the Commonwealth Fund 2014 list. And yet it far outstrips all its peers in terms of the amount it spends on healthcare – a whopping 17% of GDP.

Summary

US healthcare is not quite the Darwinian lottery imagined by foreigners. Hospitals are duty-bound to treat emergency cases. Government spending pays for a surprising share of visits to the doctor and drugs through a patchwork of public programmes: Medicare for the old, Medicaid for the poor and Chip for children. Since Obama's insurance reforms, the percentage of people who have no cover has fallen to 'only' 10% – a mere 33 million people.

For the rest, standards are generally high, sometimes among the best in the world. But no matter how good the insurance policy, few Americans can escape the crushing weight of payments bureaucracy, or the risk-averse medical practices that flow from a fear of lawsuits.

Almost all visits to the doctor (often a specialist, rather than general practitioner) will generate 'co-pays' for the patient and revenue streams for the physician that some fear encourages excessive testing and intervention: a consumer, rather than care-led, culture.

Preventive medicine and public health are harder to incentivise. Patchy access to insurance can leave emergency rooms clogged with chronic conditions. Obesity and mental illness often go entirely untreated.

Though the system fosters excellence and innovation in places, the messy combination of underinsurance and overinsurance has left the US with the highest healthcare costs in the developed world and some of the worst overall health outcomes.

Japan

Upfront payments: no

Data: Japan spends a sharply rising proportion of GDP on healthcare but falls down on the amount of time people spend in hospital, which is one of the highest among rich countries.

Summary

Every resident of Japan is required, in principle, to take out public health insurance. Regular employees are typically covered by a work scheme, and are required to pay 20% of their total medical costs at the point of delivery.

Those not covered by their employer – mainly the self-employed and unemployed – must join the national health insurance scheme. Premiums are based on salary, value of property and the number of dependants, and members pay 30% of the cost of inpatient or outpatient treatment – including emergencies – with the Government paying the remainder. People over 70 pay 10% of costs.

Medical fees above a certain ceiling – calculated depending on income and age – are paid in full by the Government. Fees are waived for uninsured people on low incomes who receive government support.

Both public insurance plans cover a range of services, including hospital care, mental health care, prescription drugs, physiotherapy and, significantly, most dental care.

The role of the state in providing healthcare services outstrips many other developed countries. In 2012, 82% of health spending was publicly funded, compared with an OECD average of 72%.

Universal health coverage has been credited with contributing to Japan's impressive longevity statistics, but the growing elderly population is adding to healthcare costs. Lengths of hospital stays are almost twice as long as in other countries.

Japan spent 8.6% of GDP on healthcare in 2008, according to OECD figures. By 2013 that had risen to 10.3%, largely because of the ballooning cost of caring for older people.

Spain

Upfront payments: no

Data: Spain has a relatively high number of doctors – and a low number of nurses – proportionate to its population, but the amount it spends on healthcare has started to fall amid the economic crisis.

Summary

Spain offers free, universal healthcare to anyone resident, legally or illegally, in the country, as well as to tourists and other visitors. Since 2012, undocumented foreigners have been entitled only to emergency care. Some 90% of Spaniards use the system, with about 18% signing up to private healthcare schemes, including many public sector workers who are given the option of free, private care. Most dental and eye care is carried out in the private sector.

The system is decentralised across the country's 17 autonomous regions and so the quality of care, and in particular access to specialist procedures or units, varies. This leads to a degree of internal health tourism. In a recent poll, medical professionals, said nine out of ten of the best hospitals were in either Madrid or Barcelona. Some regions, notably Catalonia, have implemented deeper spending cuts than others, leading to longer waiting lists and some migration towards the private sector.

Italy

Upfront payments: in some cases

Data: high doctor ratios, high numbers of pharmaceutical prescriptions.

Summary

In Italy, the national health service,

Servizio Sanitario Nazionale, offers universal health coverage that is free or low cost at the point of delivery and covers the vast majority of drugs.

It is recognised by independent experts as offering affordable and high-quality care, though there are regional differences in the standard of some state-run hospitals, with facilities in northern Italy being considered better than those in the south. Citizens can also buy private insurance, which some do to avoid waiting times for doctors' visits.

The national insurance scheme is offered to all European citizens, and includes full coverage – paid for by general taxes – of inpatient treatments, tests, medications, surgery, emergency care, paediatrics and access to a family doctor. According to Italy's health ministry, the list of pharmaceuticals that are covered by national insurance is the most complete in Europe, with patients having to pay for only products that treat minor disorders.

The ministry said Italy is also the only country in Europe that allows families to choose a paediatrician for children until age 14 at no charge.

Germany

Upfront payments: no

Data: middle of the pack. Germany was positioned fifth in the latest Commonwealth Fund rankings, spending more than the EU average on healthcare – but its lengths of stay in hospital tend to be higher than in other countries.

Summary

In Germany's healthcare system, which goes back to Otto von Bismarck's social security programme of the 1880s, anyone residing in the country is required to take out a health insurance scheme.

About 85% of the population do this by taking out insurance with one of the country's 124 non-profit Krankenkassen or 'sickness funds': public insurers, many of whom are small and linked to trade unions. Membership rates are about 15% of monthly salary, half of which is paid by employers.

Those who earn more than €4,350 (£3,300) a month can take out insurance with a private company, an option that is mainly popular with freelancers and the self-employed. For welfare recipients, health insurance membership is covered

Now, the first thing we have to check is the health of your wallet.

by local authorities.

Membership covers GP and registered specialists as well as basic dental care. If you are taken to hospital, your public health insurance kicks in once you are charged more than €10 a day, covering inpatient care with the doctor on duty at your nearest hospital.

It doesn't cover private doctors or private rooms at a hospital, homeopathic treatment or more advanced dental treatment. Patients pay for 10% of prescription drugs, with a minimum of €5 and a limit of €10 per medication per prescription.

Since 2013, patients in Germany no longer have to pay a consultation fee of €10 when seeing a doctor. They can now also go straight to a specialist, rather than waiting to be referred by a GP.

Russia

Upfront payments: no

Data: Russia has a relatively large number of doctors, but its healthcare spending is low and outcomes are generally poor.

Summary

On paper, the Russian health service is free to all. In practice, a complex compulsory medical insurance system plus low wages for doctors and nurses means that without substantial bribes, gaining a decent level of care outside the better private clinics is almost impossible. The horrific case in December in which a doctor in Belgorod punched a patient in the face, who fell to the floor and subsequently died, put the spotlight on the poor care many Russians receive.

There are many efficient and modern private clinics in Moscow, but in the regions ageing Soviet infrastructure and outdated medical practices are widespread. Medicine is widely available, and many drugs that are prescription-only in Britain are available over the counter. The Russian tendency to overprescribe means that Russians often spend huge amounts on medicines.

Emergency care is also free in theory, but private ambulances often arrive much quicker than state-provided ones, and there are also reports of ambulance crews demanding money to take patients to hospital. Most middle-class Russians have private health insurance, or simply pay upfront at private clinics when required.

Australia

Upfront payments: yes

Data: Australia scores well in comparative datasets, ranking fourth in the Commonwealth Fund table, with high numbers of doctors and average amounts of national wealth devoted to healthcare.

Summary

Most people pay to see a GP, which costs about $50–$80 (£24–£38). About half of this is reclaimable via a nationwide Medicare insurance scheme.

Some GP surgeries offer "bulk-billing", which means they only charge the reclaimable fee, so patients do not have to pay anything to see the doctor. Low-income earners and pensioners who have a government-issued healthcare card are always bulk-billed.

Most prescriptions are subsidised

through the Pharmaceutical Benefits Scheme (PBS).

Treatment in public hospitals is completely covered by Medicare, though people with private health insurance often elect to use private hospitals.

Ambulances are not covered by Medicare. Some states fund ambulances through an annual levy, though others charge $300–$2,000 (£150–£950) for an emergency ambulance callout. This goes up to $10,220 (£5,000) for an emergency callout of a helicopter in Victoria. Many people have ambulance cover as part of their health insurance.

In 2011–12, 57% of adult Australians had private health insurance, particularly older people, high earners and women in their 20s and 30s who use it for maternity care.

UK

Upfront payments: no

Data: the UK came first in the latest Commonwealth Fund assessment of healthcare systems around the rich world, but other surveys such as a European one earlier this month are not so flattering. Healthcare spending as a proportion of GDP is falling behind international averages, and an elderly demographic, the obesity epidemic and alcohol bingeing are all taking their toll. The UK also has the worst cancer outcomes of any rich country.

Summary

A mission statement set in 1948 for a universal service free at the point of use is under strain like never before. People are still able to see a GP free of charge – though booking an appointment is becoming harder. It will cost nothing to call out an ambulance and go through A&E, to undergo chemotherapy or major surgery. And yet about 11% of the population prefer to pay for private health insurance.

9 February 2016

⇨ The above information is reprinted with kind permission from *The Guardian*. Please visit www.theguardian.com for further information.

How does NHS spending compare with health spending internationally?

By John Appleby

In 2000, current spending[1] on healthcare in the United Kingdom was 6.3 per cent of GDP, and the then Prime Minister Tony Blair committed his government to matching the average for health spending as a percentage of GDP in the 14 other countries of the European Union in 2000 (8.5 per cent) through increases in NHS spending.

Over the next few years spending on the NHS increased substantially, pushing total (public plus private) spending to 8.8 per cent of GDP by 2009. By then, however, the EU-14 spend (weighted for size of GDP and health spend, and minus the UK) had moved on to 10.1 per cent of GDP. Still, the gap between the UK and its European neighbours was closing.

Since then, however, the gap has started to widen (particularly against countries that weathered the global financial crisis better than the UK) and looks set to grow further. UK GDP is forecast to grow in real terms by around 15.2 per cent between 2014/15 and 2020/21. But on current plans,[2] UK public spending on the NHS will grow by much less: 5.2 per cent. This is equivalent to around £7 billion in real terms – increasing from £135 billion in 2014/15 to £142 billion in 2020/21. As a proportion of GDP it will fall to 6.6 per cent compared to 7.3 per cent in 2014/15. But, if spending kept pace with growth in the economy, by 2020/21 the UK NHS would be spending around £158 billion at today's prices – £16 billion more than planned.

The growing gap between us and our European neighbours should give pause for thought. Tony Blair's commitment was partly an appeal to "keeping up with the Schmidts and Lefebvres". But it also emphasised that spending more on health care was affordable: if the Danes, Swedes, French and Germans can spend more on healthcare without apparently bankrupting the rest of their economy, why can't we?

Comparing spending on healthcare between countries is not straightforward. We have to consider

how to deal with differences in the source of funding: public or private (which will include out-of-pocket spending as well as insurance payments, often compulsory in countries with social insurance systems). Given differences in the way countries fund their healthcare it is usual to compare total spending (public plus private) expressed as a proportion of countries' GDP.

On this basis, data from the OECD shows that in 2013 (the latest year for which figures have been published) the UK spent 8.5 per cent of its GDP on public and private healthcare. (This excludes capital spending equivalent to 0.3 per cent of GDP to make figures comparable with other countries'.) This placed the UK 13th out of the original 15 countries of the EU and 1.7 percentage points lower than the EU-14's level (i.e. treating the whole of the EU-14 (i.e. minus the UK) as one country with one GDP and one total spend on healthcare) of 10.1 per cent of total GDP.[3] (Note: the difference of 1.7ppts is rounded.)

If we were to close this gap solely by increasing NHS spending (and assuming that health spending in other UK countries was in line with the 2015 Spending Review plans for England), by 2020/21 it would take an increase of 30 per cent – £43 billion – in real terms to match the EU-15 weighted average spend in 2013, taking total NHS spending to £185 billion.

And of course we may find that by 2020/21 the EU average has moved on, leaving the UK lagging behind its neighbours once more.

Compared to OECD countries there is also a gap. Omitting the United States (which heavily distorts the weighted average due to its relatively high health spend and its very high GDP), the OECD spend is 9.1 per cent.[4] For the UK to match this would require total spending to reach £163 billion – an additional 15 per cent or £21 billion – by 2020/21 over current spending plans.

Whether funded publicly or privately, spending more on health will necessarily mean less on other things – either less private disposable income (if the additional money comes from additional taxation) or less on other publicly funded services such as education or defence – or indeed, paying down the UK's debt and reducing its deficit. Or it means additional government borrowing (which will have to be paid for by increased tax or less spending on non-NHS services). Historically, increases in NHS spending have in the main been achieved by reduced spending on other public services (such as defence) rather than say borrowing or tax increases per se.

Whatever the flaws of international comparisons, it's clear the UK is currently a relatively low spender on health care – as the Barker Commission pointed out – with a prospect of sinking further down the international league tables. The question is increasingly not so much whether it is sustainable to spend more – after all, many countries already manage that and have done for decades. Rather, it is whether it is sustainable for our spending to remain so comparatively low, given the improvements in the quality of care and outcomes we want and expect from our health services.

Notes

[1] Except where stated, capital spending has been excluded from international comparisons as reporting is not as up to date or comprehensive as for current spending. The final estimates for UK (current plus capital) spending matching EU and OECD averages are therefore slightly underestimated.

[2] That is, using public expenditure statistical analyses for UK NHS spend figures in 2013/14 as a starting point, and assuming spending on the NHS in Scotland, Wales and Northern Ireland grows at the same rate as planned for England and set out in the government's 2015 Spending Review and Autumn Statement.

[3] The 'simple' average for the EU-14 – the average of the percentage health spends – in 2013 was 9.6 per cent.

[4] This is based on treating the OECD as one country with one GDP and one spend on health. The 'simple' average of percentage spends on health is 8.7 per cent.

20 January 2016

⇨ The above information is reprinted with kind permission from The King's Fund. Please visit www.kingsfund.org.uk for further information.

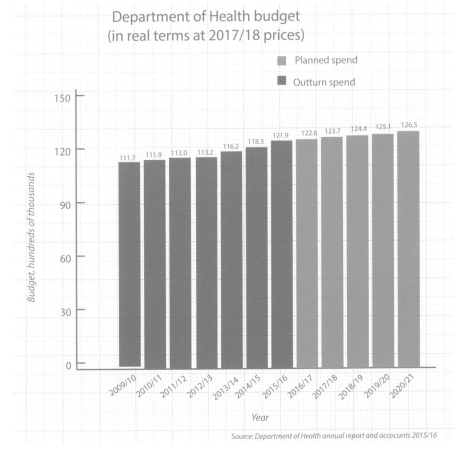

Department of Health budget
(in real terms at 2017/18 prices)

Planned spend
Outturn spend

111.7 111.9 113.0 113.2 116.2 118.3 121.9 122.6 123.7 124.4 125.1 126.5

Budget, hundreds of thousands

2009/10 2010/11 2011/12 2012/13 2013/14 2014/15 2015/16 2016/17 2017/18 2018/19 2019/20 2020/21

Year

Source: Department of Health annual report and accocunts 2015/16

Underfunded, underdoctored, overstretched: the NHS in 2016

The Royal College of Physicians (RCP) has long argued that we need to rethink the way we deliver healthcare: breaking down barriers between hospitals and the community, and working in partnership with patients to deliver joined-up care. To achieve this, we need a health service that is funded to meet the demands placed on it by our growing population.

'The NHS budget has not kept pace with rising demand for services'

This report is the first of a series in our Mission: Health campaign which will be focused on three major themes – working for health, delivering health, and creating health.

'The UK does not train enough doctors. Hospital teams are feeling the pressure of staffing gaps'

Time for action

The NHS in 2016 is under-funded, under-doctored and overstretched. Patients and communities deserve to know the true choice that we face: increase funding or cut care. The RCP believes they deserve more than that: an NHS funded and staffed to meet their needs, now and in the future. The NHS in 2016 needs a new plan – a plan designed to meet the UK's health and care needs in the long term, and to value, support and motivate NHS staff.

Increase NHS funding

The NHS budget has not kept pace with rising demand for services. We need a new NHS budget that:

⇨ meets the demand for health services

⇨ sets realistic targets for efficiency savings

⇨ protects funds for transformation

⇨ invests in the long-term sustainability of the NHS.

Train more doctors

The UK does not train enough doctors. Hospital teams are feeling the pressure of staffing gaps. That's bad for them, and it's bad for patients. We need to:

⇨ increase the number of medical students and doctors training to be hospital specialists

⇨ incentivise doctors to work in the most challenging and in-demand areas of medicine

⇨ take cross-governmental action to relieve immediate pressure on the NHS workforce.

Improve the working lives of NHS staff

Being a doctor is intense, rewarding and challenging. A cared-for workforce delivers better outcomes for patients. In late 2016, the RCP will launch a new campaign to value and support doctors working in the NHS. We will:

⇨ work with our member doctors to find new solutions to workforce pressures

⇨ push for action from across government and the NHS

⇨ showcase the very best of medicine.

21 September 2016

⇨ Reproduced from: Royal College of Physicians. *Underfunded, underdoctored, overstretched: the NHS in 2016.* www.rcplondon.ac.uk/underfunded-underdoctored-overstretched-nhs-2016.

What is the NHS budget?

Most of the National Health Service (NHS) is free to use for UK residents. The amount of money the NHS gets is decided differently across the UK as the responsibility of health and care was given to the Scottish Government, the Welsh Government and the Northern Ireland Assembly.

England

About 99% of the Department of Health's budget comes from taxes. The rest of the money comes from charges for things like prescriptions for medicine, dentists, and opticians services.

The Government plans to spend around £122 billion on health in England in 2017/18, or roughly £2,200 per person. Around £108 billion will be spent on the day-to-day running of the NHS.

The rest is spent by the Department of Health on things like public health initiatives (which aim to improve people's health so they don't need to use the NHS as often), education, training, and infrastructure (such as IT and building new hospitals).

Spending is expected to rise to £123 billion in 2020/21, of which £111 billion will be for the day-to-day running of the NHS.

Scotland

The NHS in Scotland receives almost all of its money from the Scottish Government. Unlike in England, Scottish residents don't have to pay for prescriptions for medication. It is also free to see a dentist or optician in Scotland, but there are some charges for certain treatments.

Health spending in Scotland is planned to be £13.2 billion in 2017/18, or around £2,500 per person. This includes some money for sport as well as health.

Wales

The NHS in Wales receives almost all of its money from the Welsh Government. Welsh residents don't pay for prescriptions for medication, but there are charges for visiting the dentist or the optician.

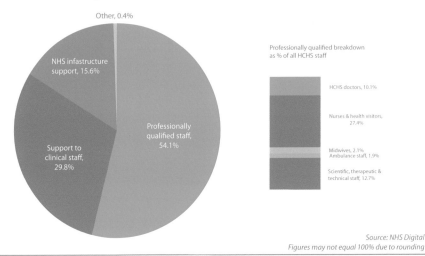

NHS hospital & community health service staff – main staff groups, January 2017, full time equivalent

Other, 0.4%

NHS infastructure support, 15.6%

Professionally qualified staff, 54.1%

Support to clinical staff, 29.8%

Professionally qualified breakdown as % of all HCHS staff

HCHS doctors, 10.1%

Nurses & health visitors, 27.4%

Midwives, 2.1%
Ambulance staff, 1.9%

Scientific, therapeutic & technical staff, 12.7%

Source: NHS Digital
Figures may not equal 100% due to rounding

Health spending in Wales is planned to be £7.3 billion in 2017/18, or roughly £2,300 per person. Like Scotland, this includes some money for sport as well as health.

Northern Ireland

In Northern Ireland the NHS is referred to as the Health and Social Care Service (HSC) and includes hospitals, GP services, and community health and social services.

The HSC receives its money from the Northern Ireland Executive. Northern Ireland residents don't have to pay for prescriptions for medication, but there are charges for visiting the dentist or the optician.

Health spending in Northern Ireland in 2016/17 was £5 billion, or roughly £2,700 per person.

1 June 2017

⇨ The above information is reprinted with kind permission from Full Fact. Please visit www.fullfact.org for further information.

© Full Fact 2017

HOW HEALTHY IS THIS BUDGET?

- ONLY AS HEALTHY AS WE ARE!

Spending on the NHS in England

Total health spending in England is nearly £124 billion in 2017/18 and is expected to rise to over £125 billion by 2020, taking inflation into account.

Around £110 billion will be spent on the day-to-day running of the NHS. The rest is spent by the Department of Health on things like public health initiatives, education, training, and infrastructure (including IT and building new hospitals).

The NHS is facing severe financial pressures, with trusts across the country spending more than they're bringing in. The NHS is also being asked to find £22 billion in savings by 2020, in order to keep up with rising demand and an ageing population.

Health experts from the Nuffield Trust, Health Foundation and King's Fund say current spending plans aren't enough to maintain standards of care, meet rising patient demand and deliver new services such as the so-called "seven-day NHS".

They also cite concerns that there isn't enough money going into social care, which we've looked at elsewhere.

The NHS faces a £30 billion funding gap by 2020

In 2013, NHS England said it faced a funding gap of £30 billion by the end of the decade, even if government spending kept up in line with inflation. So it needed that much more to deliver care to a growing and ageing population, assuming it made no savings itself.

A year later the NHS laid out plans for how it might handle this gap. One ambitious option was that the NHS itself would find £22 billion in savings, leaving the other £8 billion to be filled by the Government.

The Conservatives said in their 2015 election manifesto they would provide that £8 billion in government, and expect the other £22 billion in savings from the NHS. The Nuffield Trust, writing in our election report, said this still left unanswered questions on funding:

"£8 billion is the bare minimum to maintain existing standards of care for a growing and ageing population... improving productivity on this scale [£22 billion] would be unprecedented."

The new Conservative Government followed through on the commitment and started claiming it was giving £10 billion, giving the NHS what it asked for, and more.

The Government's "£10 billion" spending claim can't be taken at face value

The Government has previously claimed that it's putting an extra £10 billion into the NHS by 2020/21, more than NHS executives have asked for.

This isn't as generous as it sounds, and the chief executive of NHS England has directly contradicted the claim that it's getting more than it requested. The Health Select Committee has also criticised the Government for its repeated use of this figure, as have the Nuffield Trust, Health Foundation and King's Fund.

First of all, the pot of money has been redefined.

The Government's claim is just about the NHS England budget, rather than total health spending in England which includes things like public health, education and training. Funding outside the budget of NHS England is set to fall by over £3 billion from 2015/16 to 2020/21.

Secondly, the head of NHS England, Simon Stevens, has said the service isn't getting more than it asked for. He told the Public Accounts Committee of MPs recently:

"It's right that by 2020 NHS England will be getting an extra £10 billion over the course of six years. I don't think that's the same as saying we're getting more than we asked for over five years because it was a five year forward view [that the NHS set out] not a six year forward view.

"And over and above that we've obviously had a spending review negotiation in the meantime and that has set the NHS budget for the next three years.

"It's a matter of fact... that like probably every part of the public service, we got less that we asked for in that process. And so I think it would be stretching it to say that the NHS has got more than it asked for."

He also said last year that the money the government has committed is at the lowest end of a range of options the NHS set out.

'The NHS is facing severe financial pressures, with trusts across the country spending more than they're bringing in'

For it to be enough, the service also needs to see "continuing access to social care" and "enhanced effort on prevention and public health". Public health spending is expected to fall and spending on social care is set to fall short of what experts think is needed.

In 2015 the NHS itself highlighted these two areas as needing improvement.

That said, the Government is 'front loading' the spending increases over this period – meaning that more money will be made available in the early years, and comparatively smaller increases in the later years.

At present, funding in 2018/19 isn't expected to grow at all, taking inflation into account. Rises – or lack of – like these are "inadequate" and "will not be enough to maintain standards of care, meet rising demand from patients and deliver the transformation of services outlined in the NHS five year forward view" according to the Nuffield Trust, Health Foundation and King's Fund.

NHS England budget increasing, public health budget falling

The amount of money the Government spends on health in England is roughly equivalent to the Department of Health's budget, which is the same £124 billion figure we quoted above.

Within that pot of money, the Government spent about £110 billion on NHS England, which oversees the vast majority of spending, with the rest going to things like public health, education and training.

The NHS England budget is expected to rise by about £9 billion from 2015/16 to 2020/21, taking inflation into account. Meanwhile spending on the other areas is set to fall by £3.1 billion.

That means, overall, health spending in England is set to rise by £5.9 billion between 2015/16 and 2020/21.

NHS providers are in deficit

About two-thirds of NHS trusts – which provide secondary care to patients who've been referred there by a GP – are in the red.

Collectively they finished 2015/16 with a deficit of about £2.5 billion. They'd have had a bigger shortfall without measures (£) taken by NHS England and the Department of Health to shore up the finances for that year.

By contrast, central government and NHS England came in under budget, meaning that the 'net deficit' of NHS bodies was £1.85 billion overall in 2015/16.

The size of the deficit has been growing—in 2014/15 the overall deficit was £574 million.

Local deficits end up costing the Government money. The Department of Health and NHS England put in £2.4 billion in extra financial support for trusts last year, to support their deficits.

6 June 2017

⇨ The above information is reprinted with kind permission from Full Fact. Please visit www.fullfact.org for further information.

The battle to break even

Minimising the damage to the NHS while extricating it from the EU is a huge test of the new government. Can it survive the workforce, funding and regulation challenges heading its way? Tim Tonkin finds out.

The dust is now slowly settling on the 2017 general election – called by Theresa May to strengthen her hand in Brexit negotiations.

While negotiations with the EU are set to begin in earnest on 19 June, many health organisations, including the BMA, are clear that the Government can waste no time in making the NHS its main priority.

Speaking shortly before the election, BMA council chair Mark Porter stressed exactly that, with Brexit now under way and with the NHS at breaking point: "It is vital that the next Government ensures long-term stability for the NHS by granting permanent residence to EEA [European Economic Area] doctors working in the UK; maintains the current working time regulations; protects life-changing medical research which benefits from European funding; and ensures that leaving the EU will not delay the UK's access to vital pharmaceuticals."

Dr Porter's warning also came in response to a report published ahead of last week's vote by the Nuffield Trust, which argues that Brexit and the future of the UK health service are inextricably linked.

Identifying opportunities as well as risks, the report warns, above all, that prioritising healthcare in securing a good deal on leaving the EU is vital to safeguarding the short- and long-term stability of the NHS.

"There is a risk that the decision to leave the EU will amplify these pressures [on the NHS], given its potential impact on the overall size of the economy and the supply of overseas staff to health and social care services," it concludes.

"However, a departure from the EU could contain other benefits for the NHS if further funds can be found to invest in services, and changes in the regulatory framework can work to support positive change."

It adds: "Whether or not these benefits will outweigh the significant workforce and financial costs Brexit could mount on already stretched services remains to be seen and will depend largely on the NHS being recognised as a significant priority as we enter some of the most important negotiations in [the UK's] history."

Promises, promises

While the main political parties all pledged to pump additional billions into the NHS by 2022/23 in their pre-election manifestos, separate analysis by the Nuffield Trust ultimately dismisses all as inadequate in meeting the health service's forecast financial needs.

The NHS Five Year Forward View warns that the NHS will face a £22 billion funding gap by 2020, while the BMA calls for UK health spending to match the average spent by Europe's ten leading economies, equivalent to 10.4 per cent of UK GDP in 2015.

Going into negotiations with the EU, the Nuffield Trust sees a number of potential outcomes for health spending.

While dismissing the infamous £350 million-a-week pledge put forward by the Vote Leave campaign during the 2016 referendum, the report states that redirecting the bulk of UK financial contributions to the EU into the health service could make a significant difference.

With the UK's net contributions to the EU averaging £7.1 billion between 2010 and 2014, by investing "much of this money" into health, the NHS in England could theoretically benefit from an extra £5.2 billion 'with matching funds across the UK'.

However, this ideal scenario is tempered by a number of crucial caveats. The overall impact of Brexit on the UK economy could see public finances contract by £15.2 billion by

2020/21, according to the Office for Budget Responsibility.

Such a shortfall, if spread out equally across the public sector, could see the NHS in England alone having its annual spending slashed by £2.4 billion.

Compound costs

According to the report, this blow to NHS finances could be further compounded should the UK incur additional costs relating to health services post-Brexit.

"Brexit could mean that the NHS needs more money than it otherwise would,'"the trust warns. "They could include £100 million or more from a fracturing of the medicines market; as much as £1 billion for caring for pensioners who have to return to the UK; and potentially several hundred million pounds in additional pay and training to compensate for lost EU migrants."

It adds: "Many of these items could be minimised or eliminated with the right deal."

The BMA has warned that poor workforce planning, as pursued by successive previous governments, has led to huge recruitment and retention problems in the NHS workforce, particularly in areas such as general practice and emergency medicine.

42 per cent of EU doctors stated they were considering leaving the UK in a BMA survey earlier this year, a concern borne out by the trust's report, which notes signs of EEA migration already "falling sharply".

As such, guaranteeing residency rights and reciprocal arrangements for EU nationals working in the NHS has been a long-standing demand of the BMA, and both were included in its pre-election manifesto A Vote for Health.

The association has also called for the negotiation of a flexible post-Brexit immigration system that would preserve the NHS's ability to employ EU doctors and allow UK-trained doctors to work on the continent.

Figures produced by the Royal College of Nursing reveal that, last year, nearly one third of all the newly registered UK nurses had received their training in EEA countries. Added to this the Nuffield Trust's finding that EU nationals now make up seven per cent of the country's social care workforce, the importance of a Brexit deal providing flexibility over access to overseas health staff becomes clear.

Restricted movement

In its report, the trust notes that the UK could experience shortfalls of up to 20,000 nurses and 70,000 social care staff by 2025/26, if stricter immigration requirements are placed on European nationals.

"The UK has long depended disproportionately on doctors from overseas to fill medical posts ... Labour and the Conservatives agree that Brexit will mean the end of free movement of labour from Europe, a radical shift in the UK's migration policy.

"It is vital that the NHS gets a deal that helps rather than hinders it in dealing with the staffing crisis."

The trust states that such a deal could be achieved either by exempting professions such as nursing from migration restrictions or by creating a shortage occupation system for EEA migrants.

Failure to secure the necessary flexibility in migration rules could instead see a renewed emphasis on producing homegrown staff. However, the length of time in medical training would not make this a viable option in the short term.

"There will be a lag of three years between starting to train more nurses and any impact on the qualified workforce – already taking us a year past Brexit.

"Guaranteeing the safe staffing of the NHS after Brexit requires, above all, a commitment to deliver the supply of nurses the NHS needs, backstopped by a commitment to put in substantial funding if required."

"Humanitarian crisis"

Running in parallel to the NHS's staffing crisis is the challenge posed by ever-increasing patient demand and an ageing UK population.

Analysis of NHS pressures published last month by the BMA reveals the stark reality on the front line of the country's hospitals, where staff fought to keep the health system flowing smoothly and the British Red Cross warned of a "humanitarian crisis" unfolding.

Bed occupancy on general and acute wards stood at 90.6 per cent during the final three months of last year, and the number of patients waiting more than four hours while attending emergency departments during the winter of 2016–17 stood at nearly 20 per cent.

Reciprocal healthcare arrangements mean that citizens who choose to retire in other EU states receive equal healthcare rights, with the costs of this care being reimbursed by their native countries.

With around 190,000 UK pensioners living on the continent, the Department of Health pays close to £500 million in care costs to other EU states. However, the report warns that failure to negotiate a continuation of the scheme following Brexit could see these costs being doubled, as well as heaping further demand directly on to the NHS.

"If British pensioners lost their healthcare cover in EU states and had to return to the UK to get the care they need, the extra annual costs to the NHS could amount to as much as £1 billion every year."

The trust estimates that the additional staffing and infrastructure required to meet the needs of 190,000 returning UK citizens would be equivalent to two new hospitals – 900 beds and 1,600 additional health staff comprising nurses, doctors and allied professionals.

It adds that with around one million UK expats in Europe in total, these figures could be merely "the tip of an iceberg".

"It may not be easy to continue after Brexit with reciprocal health care arrangements like S1 – or the European health insurance card that covers travellers... However, it is in the best interests of the NHS to see if a continued deal can be agreed."

Free from red tape

Prior to the election, the BMA urged the Government to seek a common regulatory environment between the UK and EU regarding health, from pharmaceuticals to the standards imposed on clinical trials and research.

In its report, the Nuffield Trust warns

that exiting the EU – which as a pharmaceuticals market accounts for 25 per cent of all global medicine sales – and the European Medicines Agency would pose considerable risks.

As a smaller, separate market, the UK would potentially see delays in the introduction of new medicines, with companies prioritising approval in the larger EU market. This could in turn hinder the NHS's ability to access drugs easily and prevent shortages.

The trust does, however, note the possibility for positive legislative change in healthcare on leaving the EU.

EU laws on procurement and competition requiring NHS trusts to tender contracts openly could be ended if repealed by the Government following Brexit.

However, leaving the jurisdiction of EU law also holds risks.

Workplace protections such as the working time directive, which legally enforces maximum weekly working hours and is supported by the BMA, could also be overturned.

The BMA has staunchly backed working time directives arguing they protect patients and doctors from the dangers posed by overworked and exhausted staff.

The new Government will soon begin a two-year period of negotiations with the EU. Disentangling the UK from more than 40 years of political and economic union will naturally involve consideration being given to many areas.

Yet, with the NHS already reeling from years of poor planning and underfunding, getting the right deal on health could prove to make or break its future.

"Brexit will have a lasting impact on health and social care in the UK,' the Nuffield Trust warns. 'Getting it wrong risks leaving already strained services with an impossible task."

A student's training hangs in the balance

Brexit threatens to bring one German medical student's positive experience of living and learning in the UK to an abrupt end

'What does this all mean for me?' This is the question that I, and my parents back in Hamburg, have been asking since the UK's vote to leave the EU.

The uncertainty has replaced the feelings of denial that I had previously felt; until the triggering of Article 50 in March, Brexit had seemed distant and impersonal. Now it feels like I am increasingly having to question everything.

I first came to the UK for a gap year following school, and spent a year living in London. I enjoyed myself so much that I was more than happy to take the opportunity to return as a medical student.

Having been able to study at Cambridge and now Oxford has been a huge privilege and I would be very happy to pursue a master's or PhD and even make my career here.

Brexit, however, has put a new complexion on all of this.

The main problem is the uncertainty about what it's actually going to mean for someone like me, an EU citizen who wants to remain in the UK.

Without assurances on what kind of residency rights I might be granted in the coming years, it is easier to gear future plans around leaving the country; knowing I won't have to worry about these things if I go back to Germany or to a different [EU] country. I know that for the remainder of the time that I am studying, I am guaranteed to continue on the conditions on which I arrived here.

This means that even as an EU student I would still get to benefit from access to support such as NHS bursaries for my fifth and sixth years to cover my tuition fees.

EU students pay the same rates as UK ones, whereas the fees paid by overseas students from outside are more than three times as high and they don't get any financial support from the UK or any EU institutions.

I have a friend who is also an overseas student who did a master's here and was successful in securing a place to study for a PhD. However, because her home country is not part of the EU, she did not get the funding and could not take the opportunity to pursue this qualification.

Once Brexit is formalised, it may be that future EU students who would want to start studying here will no longer be able to access equal treatment and financial support.

If this becomes the case, I think it would be financially unbearable to start studying here now for most EU students.

As things stand, Brexit negotiations will complete the same year that I complete my studies.

While living and working in the UK as an EU citizen would have previously been a formality, I now have to consider the possibility that I may well need a visa to complete my first foundation year. Even returning to Germany to practise may not be as straightforward two years from now.

At the moment, a medical qualification gained in one EU country is recognised in another, but if the UK leaves the EU then the bureaucratic hurdle is going to be a lot higher. In my view, the Government here needs to think carefully about what kind of deal it tries to secure for the EU nationals already within its borders, and who may wish to come in future.

The expense of studying will be one of the major barriers to EU students coming to the UK post-Brexit, unless a future government takes steps to mitigate against this.

For those of us already here we continue to live with the uncertainty as to whether there is going to be any discrimination in terms of competition for training posts or jobs between 'outsiders' and UK nationals.

Torben Heinsohn is a fourth-year medical student at Oxford University. Originally from Germany, he is set to complete his medical degree as the UK's two-year Brexit negotiations with the EU come to a close.

9 June 2017

⇨ The above information is reprinted with kind permission from the British Medical Association. Please visit www.bma.org.uk for further information.

© British Medical Association 2017

Majority of people would support raising National Insurance to fund the NHS

Twice as many support raising National Insurance to boost NHS funding than oppose it.

The NHS has led the news this week. The Royal College of Nursing has branded conditions in the NHS the worst they have ever experienced, whilst the Royal College of Physicians says the health service is having to deal with its worst-ever winter crisis. In Parliament, Jeremy Corbyn slammed Theresa May for being "in denial" about the pressures the NHS is facing.

In a select committee hearing yesterday, Simon Stevens, the chief executive of NHS England, challenged the Prime Minister's view of health funding. NHS England estimated last year that its funding gap could be as high as £30 billion by 2020/21.

With extra money for the NHS needing to be found somewhere, a fortnight ago Liberal Democrat leader Tim Farron suggested that the public may be ready to pay an extra penny on income tax in order to improve health services.

New YouGov research suggests that the public are increasingly open to this idea, and are now more likely to support such a move than oppose it.

The proportion of people who would support boosting health spending by an extra penny on the basic rate of income tax has increased by eight points since April 2014, and now stands at 42%. By contrast, the level of opposition to such a move has fallen from 51% to 37% over the same time period, meaning the public is now more likely to support a tax increase to fund the health service than oppose it.

That being said, such a move is not backed by all social groups. Whilst people to the left of centre, women, middle class and older people tend to support the policy, younger people and UKIP voters tend to oppose it. Conservative voters, men and the working class are quite evenly split on the idea.

The public would prefer the policy if it applied to National Insurance

Politically speaking, the better option could be to boost NHS spending by adding an extra penny on the pound to people's National Insurance contributions. More than half of people (53%) would support such a policy, up five points since April 2014. Only about a quarter (26%) would actively oppose the move, having fallen from 37% in 2014.

The research shows that this way of increasing NHS funding enjoys a double-digit lead across all sections of society.

However, while more popular, increasing National Insurance instead of income tax could end up hitting poorer people harder. This is because even the lowest earners pay National Insurance, but the £11,000 tax-free allowance would mean increasing income tax would affect them less. Additionally, an income tax increase would see better-off pensioners contributing as well, which they would not do under a National Insurance increase.

Whichever policy change the public favour, what is clear is that the populace does not think the current state of affairs is sustainable. Support for maintaining current levels of NHS spending – leaving income tax and National Insurance levels as they are – has dropped 13 points in the last three years to just 31%.

Opposition to keeping the status quo stands six points higher at 37%, although nearly a third of people (32%) say they don't know whether they would support or oppose NHS spending levels continuing as they are.

With the Liberal Democrats still struggling somewhat in the polls, Tim Farron will doubtless be pleased to see that he has hit on a policy that is popular with the public. Now he will just have to do his best to see his party get the credit for it.

12 January 2017

⇨ The above information is reprinted with kind permission from YouGov. Please visit www.yougov.co.uk for further information.

© 2000–2017 YouGov plc

Most people would support increasing National Insurance in order to boost NHS spending

Would you support or oppose increasing the basic rate of employees' Income Tax from 20% to 21% and using the money raised to increase spending on the NHS? (%)

Support	53
Oppose	26
Don't know	21

Would you support or oppose increasing the basic rate of employees' National Insurance from 12% to 13% and using the money raised to increase spending on the NHS? (%)

Support	42
Oppose	37
Don't know	21

Source YouGov / yougov.com

Public attitudes to the NHS

An extract from NatCen's British Social Attitudes Report *2015*.

Dissatisfaction with the NHS

For more than 30 years, we have measured levels of public satisfaction with the NHS by analysing responses to the following question:

All in all, how satisfied or dissatisfied would you say you are with the way in which the National Health Service runs nowadays?

Although politicians and the media tend to focus on year-to-year changes in the public's view of the health service, by examining long-term trends we can identify broad patterns of change and the circumstances that may be encouraging or discouraging dissatisfaction.

Over the past 20 years our data paint a broadly positive picture for the NHS. In 1997, satisfaction with the NHS was at the lowest point in the survey's history, with half (50%) of the public expressing dissatisfaction. Just one year later, dissatisfaction had fallen to 36% and since the turn of the century has continued to fall, down to 18% in 2010. While correlation cannot be taken for causation, it is worth noting that the period of virtually continuous decline in dissatisfaction, between 2001 and 2010, coincided with a period of unprecedented increases in NHS funding and improvement in key performance measures such as hospital waiting times (Thorlby et al., 2010).

Nevertheless, while funding growth slowed considerably from 2010 onwards, and the decline in dissatisfaction halted, there has not been a concomitant reverse, as might have been expected. Rather levels of dissatisfaction levelled off (excepting the fall in 2014), remaining relatively low by historical standards. And although dissatisfaction rose by eight percentage points, to 23%, between 2014 and 2015 this was from a very low base, as 2014 saw the lowest level of dissatisfaction with the NHS since the survey began in 1983 (15%).

Dissatisfaction with individual services

Alongside satisfaction with the NHS, we also ask respondents for their views on five individual health care services and on social care services run by local authorities. By examining dissatisfaction with these individual services, we can begin to build a picture of what might be driving dissatisfaction with the NHS overall and the extent to which this links to dissatisfaction with particular services.

General practice has traditionally been the most popular sector with dissatisfaction levels varying far less from year to year than for the NHS overall. In 2015, 16% were dissatisfied with GPs. Despite media attention over the past few years reporting pressures in general practice, levels of dissatisfaction in 2015 are similar to those seen a decade earlier. However, there is a small but significant upward trend over the last few years with dissatisfaction rising from 12% in 2009 to 16% in 2015.

Attitudes to dentists have seen a more dramatic change. After the turn of the century, there was a steep rise in dissatisfaction, peaking at 38% in 2004. In part, this may have been attributable to increasing problems of access to NHS dental services in some areas of the country as growing numbers of dentists developed their private work at the expense of their NHS work in reaction to changes in NHS payment rates (Department of Health, 2000). Since then, and with changes in the NHS dental contract, dissatisfaction has steadily declined, down to 18% in 2015. To find lower levels of dissatisfaction, we have to look back to the 1980s and early 1990s when, for a few years, around 10% reported negative views about dentists.

Compared with the NHS overall and its individual services, dissatisfaction with social care is high – 33% express dissatisfaction in 2015. Social care is a service provided by local authorities for people who cannot look after themselves because of illness, disability or old age. The proportion who are dissatisfied has increased from a low point of 25% in 2005, when the question was first asked albeit with slightly different wording.[1] Many people are unsure about exactly what social care services are, and relatively few people have experience of using them. This perhaps accounts for the high proportion of almost one-third (31%) who report being "neither satisfied nor dissatisfied" with the service.

We also ask respondents how satisfied they are with three hospital-based services: inpatients, outpatients, and accident and emergency. Dissatisfaction levels for each of these areas has followed a broadly similar trend and tends to mirror changes in levels of dissatisfaction with the NHS overall.

While, since 2001, levels of dissatisfaction with outpatient services have been declining, down to 11% in 2015 (a slight but significant increase from the 2014 low of 8%), dissatisfaction with accident and emergency services has remained fairly flat at around 20% since 2007. On the other hand, dissatisfaction with inpatient services has tended to follow the trend for outpatients and, in 2015, recorded the second lowest level (12%) since 1983.

While we see distinct patterns in dissatisfaction with individual NHS services, dissatisfaction with hospital-based services most broadly mirrors trends in dissatisfaction with the way in which the NHS runs overall. This suggests that perceptions and experiences of these services may be important in driving levels of dissatisfaction. It is to the question of who is dissatisfied that we turn next.

Why are people dissatisfied with the NHS?

To explore the factors that underlie dissatisfaction and satisfaction with

---

1 In 2005 and 2007 we asked respondents "From your own experience, or from what you have heard, please say how satisfied or dissatisfied you are with the services provided to people who need this kind of regular help with looking after themselves whose family cannot provide it?" Between 2012 and 2015 we asked respondents "And how satisfied or dissatisfied are you with social care provided by local authorities for people who cannot look after themselves because of illness, disability or old age?"

the health service, we presented respondents who said that they were dissatisfied or satisfied with separate lists of nine reasons that could potentially explain their particular viewpoint. We asked them to pick up to three that applied to them.[2] The lists of reasons offered to explain dissatisfaction and satisfaction with the NHS are presented in Figures 1 and 2 respectively.

The most frequently cited reason for dissatisfaction is waiting times (selected by more than half of those who are dissatisfied), followed by three factors relating to resources: that there are not enough NHS staff, that the Government spends too little on the NHS, and that money is wasted in the NHS. Each of these explanations was selected by around four in ten. Only around a quarter of those who are dissatisfied said this was because of the quality of care provided by the service. No other reason was selected by more than one-fifth of those who are dissatisfied.

It is also helpful to examine why people are satisfied to identify where NHS organisations are doing well (and so distinguish the areas where the NHS needs to ensure standards are maintained if they want to retain public approval).

For the 60% who are satisfied with the NHS, the quality of NHS care is the most frequently cited reason for this satisfaction (selected by six in ten of those who are satisfied). This is closely followed by two factors relating to access to care: that the NHS is free at the point of use and the good range of services and treatments available on the NHS. The top five factors also include the attitudes and behaviour of staff, chosen by around four in ten, and short waiting times for GP or hospital appointments, selected by three in ten.

Perhaps unsurprisingly, the reasons

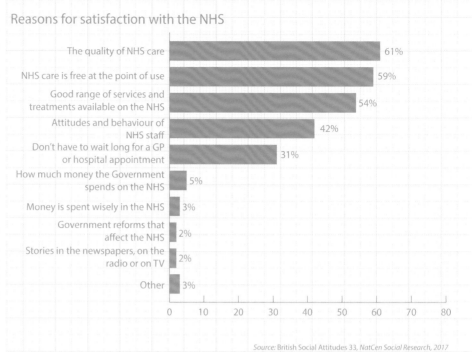

Reasons for satisfaction with the NHS

The quality of NHS care	61%
NHS care is free at the point of use	59%
Good range of services and treatments available on the NHS	54%
Attitudes and behaviour of NHS staff	42%
Don't have to wait long for a GP or hospital appointment	31%
How much money the Government spends on the NHS	5%
Money is spent wisely in the NHS	3%
Government reforms that affect the NHS	2%
Stories in the newspapers, on the radio or on TV	2%
Other	3%

0 10 20 30 40 50 60 70 80

Source: British Social Attitudes 33, *NatCen Social Research, 2017*

people give for being dissatisfied with the NHS are quite different from the reasons they cite for being satisfied. Nearly all of those who are satisfied with the NHS cite access to care as a reason (91% of satisfied respondents selected at least one of: waiting times; care being free at the point of use; the range of services and treatments available), and more than three-quarters cite quality (76% selected the quality of care or the attitudes and behaviour of staff). Very few explain their satisfaction as relating to resources, government reforms or stories in the media. This suggests satisfaction is mainly influenced by tangible factors relating to the services people use and the ease in accessing them, rather than structural and administrative factors such as decisions made by government and NHS leaders about policy and spending.

In contrast, the vast majority of people who are dissatisfied explain this on the basis of factors relating to the level of resourcing in the NHS (84% select a lack of staff, how much the government spends on the NHS or that money is wasted). A large proportion of people are also dissatisfied because of problems accessing care (this was mainly because of waiting times, but also due to the view that some services and treatments are not available). Although there has been discontent

in the health service and among politicians about the major reform program that was introduced by the Health and Social Care Act in 2012, just 18% of those who are dissatisfied identify government reforms as a causal factor.

How can the NHS placate these dissatisfied customers? The main message seems to be that the government should spend more money on the NHS – to increase capacity in general practice and the hospital sector in order to reduce waiting times, and to employ more staff. The results also point to the importance of the NHS being able to demonstrate that it has examined the efficiency of its operation, identified areas where money is wasted and acted on this. Meanwhile, the

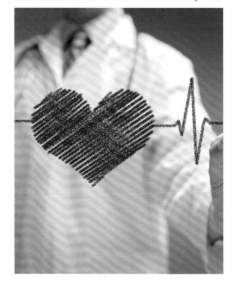

---

2 We included on the 2015 BSA survey design pilot the existing question measuring NHS satisfaction and followed this with an open-ended question asking respondents to explain the reasons for their response. We used the data obtained to develop a list of nine possible reasons for satisfaction and ten possible reasons for dissatisfaction that captured the range of different views expressed during the pilot and the language used by the public to describe these. The satisfaction and dissatisfaction lists were then tested on a second questionnaire pilot and refined.

data on reasons for satisfaction emphasise the importance of maintaining a national health service that is free at the point of need and that provides a comprehensive range of high-quality services, which can be accessed relatively quickly. These factors, which are founding principles of the NHS, seem to be closely linked to positive attitudes about the health service.

This leaves the NHS and the Government with a dilemma. Growth in the NHS budget has slowed significantly since 2010 and, over the last year, many NHS organisations have started to overspend. There is little room for NHS organisations to invest in more staff or fund the extra capacity needed to reduce waiting times further. How do the public think

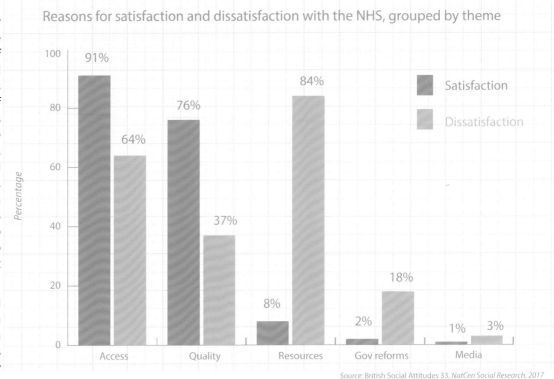

Reasons for satisfaction and dissatisfaction with the NHS, grouped by theme

Source: British Social Attitudes 33, NatCen Social Research, 2017

the Government should raise the extra money needed to address their main concerns?

For full references, please see original source.

⇨ The above information is reprinted with kind permission from NatCen Social Research. Please visit www.bsa.natcen.ac.uk for further information.

Most services meet the 'Mum Test' but there is still too much poor care, finds CQC

While the majority of services are safe and of a high quality and many are improving, too many people across England are living in care homes and receiving care and support in their own homes that is not good enough.

Without a proper recognition of the importance of adult social care and a renewed commitment to quality, the numbers of people affected by poor care could increase and have a profound impact on their lives.

In a national report, published today (Thursday 6 July 2017), the Care Quality Commission (CQC) has found that over three-quarters of adult social care services are currently rated as Good (77%, 16,351) and 2% (353) are currently rated as Outstanding.

CQC has found that strong leaders – both at provider and registered manager levels – play a pivotal role in high-performing services, where a strong vision and person-centred values inspire

staff, encouraging a culture of openness and transparency. Staff members are capable, confident and caring and are focused on supporting people to live the best lives they can.

However, CQC has found considerable variation with nearly a fifth (19%, 4,073) of services being rated as Requires Improvement and 2% (343) as Inadequate.

This is the first time that such focused analysis on a national scale has been possible following the formal introduction of CQC's new regulatory regime for adult social care in October 2014, with expert-led, specialist inspections that focus on what matters most to people using services – are they safe, caring, effective, responsive

and well-led? CQC then rates services as Outstanding, Good, Requires Improvement or Inadequate so that the public and providers are clear about its judgements.

Since then, CQC has carried out over 33,000 inspections of around 24,000 different services – many more than once. These include residential homes, nursing homes, care in people's own homes, Shared Lives schemes and supported living services. These are vital services for thousands of people, young and old, who may be living with a physical disability, learning disability, autism, dementia and/or mental health conditions.

CQC found the adult social care sector performed best in how 'caring' its services were, with 92% being rated as Good and 3% as Outstanding in this key question. In these services, CQC found staff building meaningful relationships with the people who they care for over time and treating them with compassion, kindness, dignity and respect.

Safety is where CQC has found its greatest concerns, with 23% of services being rated as Requires Improvement and 2% as Inadequate in this key question. Issues uncovered by CQC include ineffective systems and processes for managing medicines or determining staffing levels, which can result in people not getting their prescribed medicines, call bells not being answered, and home visits being rushed or missed.

CQC has used its inspections and ratings to help providers of adult social care understand the specific areas where improvements are needed, to hold them to account to make these necessary changes, to celebrate best practice and to help people to make informed choices about their care.

Already, CQC's actions are driving improvements in care for people. Of the 686 services that were originally rated as Inadequate and have been re-inspected, more than four in five (81%, 553) improved their overall rating. However, this does still mean that nearly a fifth of services have not improved and further action is required.

CQC has not seen the same rate of improvement in services that were rated as Requires Improvement initially, where only 56% of the services eventually improved to Good, with others failing to improve and some deteriorating.

Worryingly, 26% of the services that were first rated as Good and have been re-inspected have deteriorated. While these are a small proportion of services that were originally rated as Good, it shows that providers cannot always sustain this level of good practice within their services and that, as a whole, the sector continues to be fragile at a time when more people are expected to need its services.

Andrea Sutcliffe, Chief Inspector of Adult Social Care at the Care Quality Commission, said: "When CQC began to transform its regulation of adult social care in England, I asked my staff to consider whether every service they were inspecting was good enough for their Mum or anyone they loved. The 'Mum Test' has guided our work ever since and made sure that we always focus on the people who are most important – people who use services, their families and carers.

"Having carried out over 33,000 inspections of around 24,000 different services, most of the adult social care sector is meeting the Mum Test, providing safe and high quality care that we would be happy for anyone we love, or ourselves, to receive. This is thanks to the thousands of dedicated staff and providers who work tirelessly to ensure people's care is truly person-centred and meets their individual needs.

"However, there is still too much poor care, some providers are failing to improve, and there is even some deterioration.

"It appears to be increasingly difficult for some providers to deliver the safe, high quality and compassionate care people deserve and have every right to expect. With demand for social care expected to rise over the next two decades, this is more worrying than ever.

"Last October, CQC gave a stark warning that adult social care was approaching a tipping point. This was driven by more people with increasingly complex conditions needing care but in a challenging economic climate, facing greater difficulties in accessing the care they need.

"While this report focuses on our assessment of quality and not on the wider context, with the deterioration we are seeing in services rated as Good together with the struggle to improve for those with Inadequate and Requires Improvement ratings, the danger of adult social care approaching its tipping point has not disappeared. If it tips, it will mean even more poor care, less choice and more unmet need for people.

"The announcement in the Chancellor's budget statement of £2 billion additional funding over the next three years is welcome but even more welcome is the promise of a government consultation this year, which hopefully will lead to a long-term solution to support good quality, person-centred adult social care, both now and into the future.

"Quality must be at the heart of the long term reform of social care in England. CQC will continue to keep its relentless focus on quality with regulation becoming more targeted, risk-based and intelligence-driven over the next few years. But we cannot do it alone. Everyone must play their part in making sure quality matters and that adult social care services provide care that we would all be happy to use."

Margaret Willcox, President of the Association of Directors of Adult Social Services (ADASS), said: "This report recognises that there is a lot of great care provided by committed leaders and staff through high quality services to people in care homes and in their own home.

"Our recent 2017 budget survey shows that whilst extra funding is very welcome, it doesn't meet increasing needs and costs, that 74 per cent of directors report that providers face quality challenges and that 69 per cent of councils had experienced provider failure or returned contracts.

"The risk of adult social care approaching its tipping point is still real and we will focus on re-doubling our mutual efforts to ensure that the quality of care doesn't deteriorate and that older and disabled people and their families get the reliable, personal care they need and deserve."

6 July 2017

⇨ The above information is reprinted with kind permission from the Care Quality Commission. Please visit www.cqc.org.uk for further information.

Healthcare cuts leave patients in "disgraceful" pain

Healthcare leaders plan to delay or cancel spending in half of areas to meet financial targets – leaving patients waiting in "disgraceful" pain and uncertainty.

The King's Fund's quarterly monitoring report, which surveys financial leads at CCGs (clinical commissioning groups) around the country, found that achieving the demanded savings for the year ahead will mean "tough decisions" which will have a "direct impact" on patients.

"Our health and social care systems can no longer cope without urgent action. In the run-up to the general election, we [called] on politicians of all parties not to duck this crisis any longer"

The report found that 50 per cent of CCG finance leads felt delaying or cancelling spending would be needed.

More than 40 per cent would have to review or reduce the level of planned treatment they commission after the 18-week referral-to-treatment target was downgraded.

Just under half of CCG leaders said they were "uncertain" or "concerned" about their ability to increase funding for mental health services – despite promises of investment and focus from politicians and national health leaders.

BMA council chair Mark Porter said: "Our health and social care systems can no longer cope without urgent action. In the run-up to the general election, we [called] on politicians of all parties not to duck this crisis any longer.

"This means, as a minimum, immediately bringing investment in line with other leading European countries and outlining credible, long-term plans that will safeguard the future of the fully funded and supported NHS that staff want and patients deserve."

Rationing on the up

King's Fund chief executive Chris Ham said: "The NHS is approaching a crisis. Hospitals have been under huge pressure this winter, social care is already in crisis because of rising demand and constrained resources, and increasingly we are seeing rationing of healthcare.

"If there is no more money after the election we will see more rationing, patients will suffer, staff will feel under even greater pressure and quality of care will undoubtedly be affected."

The survey, which also covered NHS trust finance directors, suggests that NHS finances improved over the last quarter of 2016/17, with 54 per cent of finance directors expecting to have ended the year in surplus – a significant increase from those forecasting the same three months ago.

But the report suggests that the underlying financial position remains "gloomy", with many trusts having relied on one-off actions such as land sales and payments from the sustainability and transformation fund (additional central funding conditional on targets being met) to improve their position.

King's Fund director of policy Richard Murray said: "While the financial picture improved at the end of the last financial year, much of this is down to one-off actions such as selling land.

"The high levels of concern about the year ahead suggest that NHS providers are again likely to run up a significant deficit in 2017/18, a year when the sector is supposed to be in balance."

9 June 2017

⇨ The above information is reprinted with kind permission from the British Medical Association. Please visit www.bma/org.uk for further information.

© British Medical Association 2017

Is the NHS in crisis?

"Why is the NHS in crisis?" is one of the most-googled questions on the NHS this election. But is our health service really in crisis? We joined up with the independent health experts Nuffield Trust to find out.

We can't go on like this. That was the stark message of a special House of Lords Committee on the future of the NHS:

"Our conclusion could not be clearer. Is the NHS and adult social care system sustainable? Yes, it is. Is it sustainable as it is today? No, it is not. Things need to change."

They reported that: "Many of our witnesses portrayed an NHS which is now at breaking point."

There are so many ways of measuring success in the NHS, across the different countries of the UK, that it will almost always be possible to find something to boast about and something to worry about. And the NHS probably does not have a single breaking point among all its different organisations and functions.

The Nuffield Trust, a leading health think tank, has looked across:

⇨ Access to care – how many people are receiving care, how quickly?

⇨ The money – NHS Finances

⇨ The people – NHS staff

The results – how patients are doing

The results show that the NHS does face significant problems in many different areas. It is succeeding in treating more patients than in the past, but this rise in need for care, and rising costs coupled with tight budgets, are translating into widespread pressures on the ability of staff and managers to keep up with past performance and the standards the service sets itself.

Access to care is getting more difficult

Waiting times are important to patients and are a key signal of how well access to healthcare is holding up. Two particularly significant measures of waiting times in the NHS are the time people wait to get a decision in A&E about where they go next, and the time people wait from a GP referral to planned treatment. While there are many other targets, these targets are notable for their breadth: they cross all conditions, and apply in one form or another across the UK.

Wales, Scotland, Northern Ireland and England all have a goal that 95% of patients who come to A&E should have a decision taken about where they go next within four hours. The aim is to limit the time people wait in the emergency department before they are sent home, sent into the main hospital, or transferred to another service.

At one time or another over the last decade, this level of performance was achieved in Wales, Scotland and England. Now, all four countries are currently below it. As the chart below shows, there has been a gradual reduction in performance for the last five years. Even Scotland, which has kept performance fairly steady, has never managed to meet the target in winter when pressure tends to be higher.

For planned procedures like hip surgery the different health services have different targets, but again the signs of pressure are clear. Scotland and England are falling short of their commitments to treat nearly all patients within 18 weeks. Wales aims to treat patients within 26 weeks, but is not achieving this either.

six out of ten junior doctors say that poor availability of out-of-hospital care is putting patient safety at serious risk

Patient safety: the junior doctors' perspective

Junior doctors were asked whether a number of issues were having a negative impact on patient safety in their place of work. The ten highest rated* factors were:

61%	58%	52%	51%	50%	50%	46%	41%	24%	22%
Poor availability of out-of-hospital care	Lack of available hospital beds	Junior doctor rota gaps	Nursing rota gaps	Use of medical outlier systems	Staff morale	Poor rationalisation of trainees' responsibilities	Excessive administrative work	Lack of out-of-hours diagnostic services	Consultant rota gaps

Percentages of respondents who rated factors as having a serious or extremely serious negative impact on patient safety in their place of work

trainees report that a shortage of available hospital beds is putting patient safety at serious risk **six out of ten**

Source: Royal College of Physicians December 2016

These lengthening queues for treatment are happening despite the NHS treating more patients. In England, Scotland, Wales and Northern Ireland, the number of episodes of care provided in NHS hospitals has been rising. In England, for example, the number of episodes of care overseen by a hospital consultant has risen 11.4% between 2010/11 and 2015/16. It is just that the rise in the treatment provided is not keeping pace with the even faster rise in the number of people coming forward.

At the same time, England, Scotland and Wales have all started in different ways to look at reducing the provision of treatments deemed to be of less benefit to patients. That means that some people who would have got treatment on the NHS before might not in future.

Outcomes and effectiveness

Of course, access to care is not all that matters: the experience patients have, and the effectiveness of the care they do eventually get, are at least as important.

Here, there are better signs. Public satisfaction with services across the UK is holding up well, and at a relatively high level historically. The Nuffield Trust's QualityWatch review of the NHS in England with the Health Foundation last year found signs that satisfaction from patients was also being sustained, although this is measured in many different ways across the UK.

Our report also found that care for hip fractures and stroke was still improving: more recent work has found that indicators of clinical standards in ambulance treatment are also improving or being maintained. In Scotland the NHS has set reduced mortality in hospital as an important measure of health service performance. This, too, is continuing to improve.

Services are financially overstretched

This decade health services have seen some of the lowest spending increases in their history. In England, real annual increases are only around 1% a year. Real terms spending has also been roughly flat per person since 2010 in Wales, Scotland and Northern Ireland.

This compares to an average increase of nearly 4% over the history of the NHS reflecting the fact that, as the OBR has found, an aging population, new technology and rising wealth all tend to increase health spending in a country.

Yet the amount of care being provided is still rising at over 3%, and prices in health care have usually risen more rapidly than in the wider economy. For example, the English regulator NHS Improvement believes the price of drugs will rise at more than 4% for most of the next five years, whereas prices across the board are projected by the Treasury to rise at less than 2%.

Efficiency drives are underway across the UK. However, there are signs that the NHS is not keeping up with the scale of the pressure. In England, NHS trusts are on track to overspend by more than a billion pounds this year. Similar overspending is visible in Scotland and Wales.

In a sense, these problems are not surprising. As the House of Lords Committee noted "The UK has historically spent less on health when compared with the Organisation for Economic Co-operation and Development (OECD) averages. UK health spending per head is markedly lower than other countries such as France, Germany, Sweden and The Netherlands." The Committee concluded that after 2020, health spending will need to start increasing more quickly again, at least in line with overall national income. That, they say, means "a shift in government priorities or increases in taxation." The Nuffield Trust has looked at the financial implications and believes this would be sustainable.

Staff are in short supply

At the same time, the NHS is experiencing staffing shortages in key areas. These add to the pressure on services and have created an increased need for agency staffing in Scotland, England and Wales. In each country, regulators and independent bodies have expressed concern that agency staff are typically far more expensive, increasing financial pressure.

Nursing shortages leading to unfilled vacancies have become a serious issue across the UK. The Migration Advisory Committee found that as

of 2015, 31,000 posts (or around 9%) were not filled in England alone. They agreed to formally list nursing as a Shortage Occupation for immigration purposes.

Vacancies are a serious issue in general practice as well, with one GP post vacant for every two practices in the limited number reporting data in England. Even as the number of appointments is estimated to be rising, latest figures show that the number of GPs fell in 2016 in both England and Scotland. There are similar problems with practice nurses. This is a particular concern given that all health services aim to provide more care outside hospital.

The Government is trying to get more medical graduates to become GP trainees, aiming to have 5,000 extra GPs by 2020. They also hope to increase the number of nursing training places, funding this by introducing tuition fees for courses that were previously publicly funded.

However, introducing fees for nursing seems to have reduced applications in the short term – although there are still more applications than places – and drives to persuade more people to train as GPs have fallen short for several years. In the meantime the UK is bringing in over 9,000 nurses from the EU each year, which may be harder after Brexit.

Long-standing concerns about the morale and engagement of staff may feed into this problem. Surveys of NHS workers for Scotland, Wales and England all show that on the whole staff disagree that there are enough staff for people to do their jobs properly, although there has been a slight improvement in recent years. Data for England shows that the number of staff giving work-life balance as a reason for their resignation has doubled between 2012/13 and 2015/16.

30 May 2017

⇨ The above information is reprinted with kind permission from Full Fact and the Nuffield Trust. Please visit www.fullfact.org for further information.

© Full Fact/Nuffield Trust 2017

What do we die from?

The Office for National Statistics looks at the leading causes of deaths registered in England and Wales by age and sex in 2014.

There were 501,424 deaths registered in 2014, this represents a decrease of 5,366 deaths compared with 2013, a fall of 1.1%.

Top five leading causes of death account for 41% of all deaths

Ischaemic heart diseases continue to be the leading cause of death in England and Wales, accounting for 12.1% of deaths registered in 2014, compared with 19.9% in 2001.[1]

Dementia and Alzheimer disease has been the second leading cause of death since 2011 in England and Wales (10.3% of deaths in 2014, 7.8% in 2011 and 3.2% in 2001). Some of the rise since 2001 is due to an update to the coding framework used for cause of death and a better understanding of dementia; a consequence of the latter is likely to be increased reporting of dementia on death certificates.

Cerebrovascular diseases, which includes strokes, were the third leading cause of death in 2014. Lung cancer was fourth. Fifth was chronic lower respiratory diseases (which includes emphysema/bronchitis).

Twice as many women died from dementia and Alzheimer disease than men.

Heart diseases were the leading cause of death for men in 2014 (14.8% of male deaths), while for women it was dementia and Alzheimer disease (13.4% of female deaths).

The number of deaths attributable to these top two leading causes of death differs significantly for men and women. For every 100 women who died of heart diseases, 150 men died. But, for every 100 women dying from dementia and Alzheimer disease, 50 men died.

Studies suggest biological and behavioural reasons for the higher number of male deaths from heart diseases, such as a higher percentage of men who smoke and drink. In addition,

men are less likely than women to visit the doctor, leading to later diagnosis and treatment. Studies have also linked oestrogen in pre-menopausal women to the lower incidence of heart disease in women.

The likelihood of developing dementia and Alzheimer disease increases with age. As female life expectancy is greater than male life expectancy, women are more likely to survive to older ages, where they are at increased risk of developing dementia and Alzheimer disease. Scientists have shown, however, that even when correcting for age, women are at greater risk from dementia and Alzheimer. It is not yet clear why.

One in 1,000 deaths were among children aged one to four in 2014

Around 0.1% of all deaths were among children aged 1 to 4 (271 boys and 198 girls). The leading cause of death at this age (13.7% of boys and 13.1% of girls) was congenital malformations, deformations and chromosomal

1. We have used the World Health Organization's (WHO) Tenth Revision of the International Classification of Diseases (ICD-10) for coding cause of death since January 2001. Between January 2001 and December 2010, the Mortality Medical Data System (MMDS) ICD-10 version 2001.2 software provided by the United States National Center for Health Statistics (NCHS) was used to code cause of death. In January 2011, this was updated to version 2010, which incorporated most of the WHO amendments authorised up to 2009. On 1 January 2014, ONS changed the software used to code cause of death to a package called IRIS (version 2013). The development of IRIS was supported by Eurostat, the statistical office of the European Union, and is now managed by the IRIS Institute hosted by the German Institute of Medical Documentation and Information in Cologne. IRIS software version 2013 incorporates all official updates to ICD-10 approved by WHO, which were timetabled for implementation before 2014.

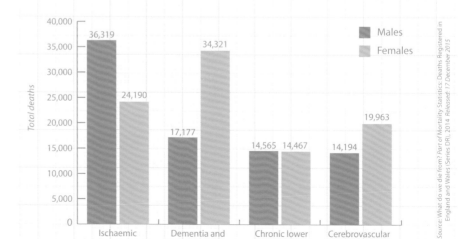

Leading causes of deaths registered in England and Wales, 2014

Source: What do we die from? Part of Mortality Statistics: Deaths Registered in England and Wales (Series DR), 2014 Released: 17 December 2015

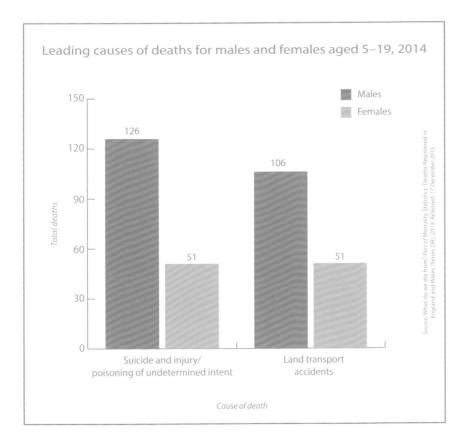

Leading causes of deaths for males and females aged 5–19, 2014

Males
Females

126

106

51

51

Total deaths

Suicide and injury/
poisoning of undetermined intent

Land transport
accidents

Cause of death

Source: *What do we die from? Part of Mortality Statistics: Deaths Registered in England and Wales (Series DR), 2014 Released: 17 December 2015*

abnormalities (including congenital heart defects and Down's Syndrome). These conditions are usually present at birth, or develop shortly after.

Land transport accidents leading cause of death for females aged five to 19

In 2014, 871 boys and 542 girls died aged five to 19. Suicide, including injury or poisoning of undetermined intent, combined with land transport accidents, accounted for one in four deaths among males and one in five deaths among females in this age group in 2014. Worldwide, road traffic injuries are the leading cause of death among young people aged 15 to 29.

Nearly four times as many men aged 20 to 34 died as a result of suicide and injury or poisoning of undetermined intent than women

Twice as many men than women died at ages 20 to 34 in 2014 (3,678 men and 1,832 women). Suicide, including injury or poisoning of undetermined intent, was the leading cause of death for persons aged 20 to 34 (23.6% of men and 13.2% of women).

For both sexes, accidental poisoning was also a highly common cause of death, followed by land transport accidents.

Breast cancer leading cause of death for women aged 35 to 49

Nearly two-thirds of deaths at ages 35 to 49 in 2014 were to men (10,407 male deaths and 6,609 female deaths).

Breast cancer was the leading cause of death for women, accounting for 13.6% of female deaths in this age group. Although breast cancer was the leading cause of death for women in this age group, breast cancer deaths among women aged 15 to 49 account for 9.7% of all female breast cancer deaths overall.

Suicide remains the leading cause of death for men aged 35 to 49, accounting for 12.6% of male deaths. Heart diseases were one of the leading causes of death for both men (second) and women (fifth) in this age group.

Heart diseases leading cause of death for men aged 50 and over and lung cancer leading cause of death for women aged 50 to 64

In 2014, 31,054 men and 21,034 women died aged 50 to 64. At these ages, the leading causes of death for both men and women were long-term diseases and conditions. Lung cancer was the number one cause for women aged 50 to 64, accounting for 11.7% of deaths in this group. Breast cancer was the second leading cause of death for women aged

50 to 64, accounting for 10.6% of deaths in this group.

For males, heart disease was the leading cause of death at ages 50 to 64, ages 65 to 79 and ages 80 and over. The number of male deaths from suicides has decreased at these ages while deaths from other diseases and conditions increase.

Heart diseases remain the leading cause of death for men aged 65 to 79, accounting for 16.0% of male deaths. Lifestyle choices and other conditions can lead to heart disease, such as: smoking, high cholesterol, high blood pressure and diabetes. For women, lung cancer remains the leading cause of death and accounts for 10.6% of all female deaths at this age. Dementia and Alzheimer disease (ranked sixth for this age group in 2013) replaced breast cancer as the fifth leading cause of death for women in 2014, accounting for 5.4% of female deaths at ages 65 to 79.

Dementia and Alzheimer disease leading cause of death for women aged 80 and over

At ages 80 and over, deaths to women exceed those to men, with 114,600 male deaths and 162,715 female deaths in 2014. Dementia and Alzheimer disease was the leading cause of death for women aged 80 and over, accounting for 19.0% of deaths. It was also the second leading cause for men, causing 12.3% of deaths in this age group.

The leading cause of death for men aged 80 and over was heart diseases, accounting for 14.3% of deaths. This was the second leading cause for women, causing 10.3% of deaths.

Where can I find out more about leading causes of death statistics?

The complete data for this release is available on our website. The leading causes of death in the world for 2002 and 2012 can be found on the World Health Organization website.

17 December 2015

⇨ The above information is reprinted with kind permission from the Office for National Statistics. Please visit www.ons.gov.uk for further information.

© Office for National Statistics 2017

NHS to show parents how fat their child will become under 'shock tactics' to fight obesity

By Laura Donnelly

The NHS is to use shock tactics in an attempt to scare parents into tackling their child's looming obesity.

Parents will be shown 3D models showing just how overweight their child is set to become by the time they reach adulthood.

Trials involving almost 3,000 children have found that the forecasts terrified families into taking action. In the pilot schemes, parents of children aged five and six were asked to key in their child's measurements.

They were then asked to watch a series of 3D graphics, showing a child their own age, digitally manipulated to look underweight, normal, overweight or obese.

After close examination from every angle, they were asked to pick which one was most like their own child.

The studies found parents routinely underestimated the size of their offspring, commonly assessing them to be the same bulk as a far-slimmer child.

When they were then shown a further model, showing what their child would look like as an adult, based on their current Body Mass Index, families were shocked into making major changes. A year later, those subject to the intervention weighed nine pounds less than those who were not.

Lead researcher Dr Angela Jones, from Newcastle University, said: "Parents play a key role because of how they shape children's health behaviour.

"They are also relied upon to recognise that their children are an unhealthy weight and take appropriate action. But we know that parents tend not to recognise when their children is overweight or obese."

She said parents tended not to realise their children were overweight because they would compare them with others in the playground, not realising how common it was for pupils to weigh too much.

Experts said the tool was a way to demonstrate to parents that children were unlikely to "grow out of" weight problems, and were on course to become overweight or obese adults.

It has now been tested in 15 areas, with proposals to roll it out on the NHS' main website, for GPs and families to use.

Paul Aveyard, Professor of Behavioural Medicine from Oxford University, said: "It gets round the problem that people don't think their child is overweight and they will grow out of it, when we know that's not really true. It's quite a striking result and it's cost free."

Susan Jebb, a Government advisor on obesity, said the future projections were key to giving parents a wake-up call.

"Seeing it projected forward [to adulthood] really personalises it for your child," said Professor Jebb, a nutrition scientist from Oxford University.

"If you can show what your child looks like as an adult you can think 'this is the kind of person who looks like they're going to have a heart attack'," she added.

Chris Snowdon, Head of Lifestyle Economic, at the Institute of Economic Affairs, said: "Parents can recognise whether their children are overweight without intrusive nannying from their GP. Doctors should already be identifying obesity and warning of the associated health risks, regardless of age. Initiatives like these waste time which the NHS simply cannot afford."

20 May 2017

⇨ The above information is reprinted with kind permission from *The Telegraph*. Please visit www.telegraph.co.uk for further information.

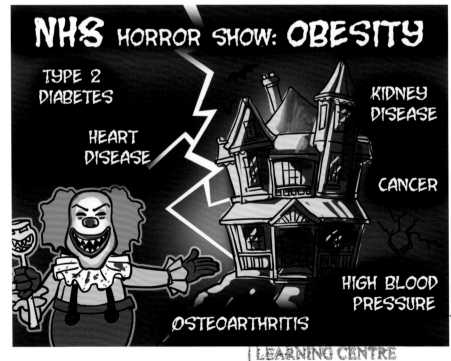

Air pollution could be ruining your sleep

Air pollution is linked to an estimated 40,000 early deaths a year.

By Thomas Tambyln and Alexandra Britton

People living in areas with high levels of air pollution have been found to be up to 60% more likely to suffer from sleep deprivation than those living with lower pollution levels, research has found.

The study, which involved 1,863 people, suggested that the impact of air pollution on a person's respiratory and central nervous system was so severe that it could ultimately affect how well we sleep.

Assistant professor of medicine at the University of Washington Martha Billings is the study's lead author.

"Prior studies have shown that air pollution impacts heart health and affects breathing and lung function, but less is known about whether air pollution affects sleep," explained Billings.

"We thought an effect was likely given that air pollution causes upper airway irritation, swelling and congestion, and may also affect the central nervous system and brain areas that control breathing patterns and sleep.

"These new findings indicate the possibility that commonly experienced levels of air pollution not only affect heart and lung disease, but also sleep quality. Improving air quality may be one way to enhance sleep health and perhaps reduce health disparities."

The study – presented at the American Thoracic Society's international conference – measured the impact of nitrogen dioxide and small particulate matter on the sample of people who had an average age of 63.

Researchers gathered air quality information from six cities in the US to gauge levels of pollution at the homes of participants and also used sleep monitoring system to measure movements.

They took participants' age, body mass, any sleep problems, ethnicity, income, smoking status and neighbourhood wealth into account when drawing up their conclusions.

The Government published long-awaited plans to cut illegal pollution two weeks ago but critics have warned they are too weak to improve the UK's dirty air.

The plans suggest measures ranging from a "targeted" scrappage scheme to take the most-polluting vehicles off the road and retrofitting local bus and lorry fleets, to removing road humps to improve traffic flow, and encouraging more electric cars.

Air pollution is linked to an estimated 40,000 early deaths a year and 37 out of 43 areas across the UK are exceeding legal European Union limits for key pollutant nitrogen dioxide, much of which comes from diesel engines.

25 May 2017

⇨ The above information is reprinted with kind permission from the Press Association. Please visit www.pressassociation.com for further information.

© Press Association 2017

New study reveals triggers for loneliness epidemic in the UK

⇨ New in-depth study by the Co-op and the British Red Cross reveals epidemic levels of loneliness and social isolation in the UK.

⇨ Over nine million[1] people in the UK (almost one fifth of the population) report they are always or often lonely.

⇨ Life transitions can be key triggers for loneliness such as becoming a new mum, empty nest syndrome or retirement, long-term health issues or mobility limitations, bereavement, and divorce or separation

⇨ Without the right support, loneliness can transition from a temporary situation to a chronic issue and can contribute to poor health and pressure on public services.

⇨ Study found loneliness is made worse by difficulties accessing public services and support, disappearance of social spaces and inadequate transport infrastructure

⇨ The partnership is calling for everyone to play a role in preventing loneliness in their communities

⇨ The British Red Cross is responding with new services funded by Co-op to provide vital support to reach over 12,000 adults who are suffering from loneliness in the UK.

⇨ The Co-op is also enhancing its services and membership offer to help tackle issue.

A new in-depth study published today (8 December) from the Co-op and British

Red Cross reveals that over nine million[2] people, across all adult ages in the UK – more than the population of London – are either always or often lonely.

The report *Trapped in a Bubble* provides a striking snapshot into modern-day loneliness and identifies six common lifetime events that can trigger loneliness and social isolation. The study debunks the widely held view that it is primarily an issue affecting older people and highlights people may experience loneliness at many different stages of their lives.

According to the survey more than half the population (52 per cent) are at the very least sometimes lonely, while only one in five (20 per cent) say that they have never felt alone. Worryingly, three-quarters (75 per cent) of those who are lonely on a regular basis do not know where to turn for support, with many feeling there is a stigma attached to admitting feelings of loneliness, which makes it hard for them to seek help.

Key triggers that can disrupt lives and create a situation in which loneliness becomes the norm include becoming a new mum at a young age, facing empty nest syndrome or retirement, experiencing long-term health issues or mobility limitations, dealing with bereavement and going through a family breakdown, such as divorce or separation.

Nearly three quarters (73 per cent) of those who are always, or often lonely have experienced at least one of the loneliness triggers. A third (33 per cent) are separated or divorced, 32 per cent suffer from long-term health conditions, while 30 per cent have mobility issues that affect their ability to move freely and easily. Nearly a fifth (19 per cent) have recently been bereaved.

The research found that community factors can cause loneliness and contribute to a person's feelings of disconnection. Loneliness in the community context is made worse by the difficulty people experience when

accessing statutory services and support, the rapid disappearance of social spaces and inadequate transport infrastructure. Participants in the research highlight these gaps that made it harder for them to find positive and effective support.

Studies show loneliness can be as damaging to health as smoking and obesity. Social isolation can also be linked to cardiovascular health risks, poor diet, heavy drinking and increased blood pressure, signs of ageing, risks of dementia, symptoms of depression and re-hospitalisation after illness. The impacts on services show loneliness could cost up to £12,000 per person over the next 15 years in increased use of public services.[3]

Following a decisive vote by its members and colleagues last year, the Co-op launched a campaign with the British Red Cross to help tackle this major issue in the UK. Fundraising by the Co-op has already passed the initial target of £3.5 million in just a year, and is now aiming for a revised target of £5 million, allowing the British Red Cross to support even more people.

Thanks to the fundraising efforts of Co-op colleagues, members and customers, from 2017 for two years the British Red Cross will provide direct, personalised support for 12,500 people experiencing loneliness or social isolation across all four nations of the UK. Brand new teams of dedicated community connectors and support at home staff and volunteers will deliver new services in 39 locations, from the north of Scotland to the west of Cornwall.

Community connectors are specialists in psychosocial support, safeguarding and supporting people experiencing loneliness and social isolation. They and their teams of volunteers will provide 12 weeks of intensive, person-centred care - identifying relevant activities, interest groups and services in a local area to help people gain confidence.

---

1 9,439,792.20 million people lonely = (UK adult 16+population 52,443,290) / 100 x 18% = 9,439,792.20
http://www.ons.gov.uk/ peoplepopulationandcommunity/ populationandmigration/populationestimates/ articles/overviewoftheukpopulation/ february2016
ONS UK population: https://www.ons. gov.uk/peoplepopulationandcommunity/ populationandmigration/populationestimates Population of London as of 2016 8.70 million - http://ukpopulation2016.com/population-of-london-in-2016.html

2 Ibid

3 Fulton and Jupp (2015) attempt to quantify the financial impact of loneliness in terms of increased service usage by older people, and estimated that this could cost up to £12,000 per person over the next 15 years.

Support at home services will also be offered in four regions to support people identified as being at risk of chronic loneliness. Staff and volunteers will provide immediate support for people who do not know where to turn for help.

In 2017, the Co-op also intends to provide a range of new services, in response to the research. Co-op Funeralcare will expand and develop its social groups for the bereaved, providing thousands of people across the country with on-going care and social support, at a crucial time in their lives. Whilst the insurance arm, in partnership with Neighbourhood Watch, is looking to refresh and expand the network in order to help strengthen and bring communities and neighbours together.

In addition to this the Co-op will also support its colleagues who may be experiencing loneliness or who are in one of the trigger groups via an enhanced employee assistance programme and pre-retirement support.

Meanwhile, the Co-op's new Membership proposition will support thousands of community groups across the UK and Co-op members will be provided with opportunities to volunteer to support British Red Cross services that tackle loneliness so they can actively support people who are experiencing loneliness in their communities.

Richard Pennycook, Chief Executive of the Co-op, said: "We already know that aging can be a risk factor for loneliness but this report clearly identifies how ordinary events in life, have the potential to disrupt our social connections and can lead to individuals becoming lonely.

"This rich insight clearly shows that there is a role for businesses, individuals and community groups to play in preventing and responding to loneliness. Having identified the trigger groups we can act much earlier to prevent loneliness potentially becoming a chronic issue for many. It is clear that a lack of support for community groups, can leave those experiencing loneliness with limited options to re-establish social connections.

"Our 70,000 colleagues, supported by members in the 1,500 communities in which we operate, have already shown their support for this important issue by enthusiastically raising money to fund British Red Cross services and that support will continue. In addition we will introduce new business approaches to support those either experiencing loneliness or at risk to the triggers of loneliness."

Mike Adamson, Chief Executive of British Red Cross UK said: "The British Red Cross supports thousands of people each year who are vulnerable and isolated. Every day our staff and volunteers see first-hand the damaging effects loneliness and social isolation have on people, many of whom are already in crisis.

"Loneliness is not only hurting individuals by making them feel disconnected from themselves and their communities – it's hurting our public services too. When left ignored, loneliness can contribute to poor health, ultimately leading to an unnecessary loss in independence and the need for more formal support.

"This is a crisis we cannot ignore, but if we come together it's also a problem we can solve. Our research shows that life transitions are key triggers for loneliness. We need to focus on these moments and work together to prevent loneliness from taking hold in the first place, by responding quickly and helping people to recover once they've hit crisis point."

8 December 2016

⇨ The above information is reprinted with kind permission from the British Red Cross. Please visit www.redcross.org.uk for further information.

Healthy behaviours

In this article, The King's Fund explores some of the most significant health-related behaviours, their impact on our health and wellbeing, and how they are changing over time in England. We also look at how some behaviours vary with people's socio-economic status.

Key messages

Current lifestyles present a serious threat to population health, particularly for more disadvantaged groups

66 per cent of the adult population are not meeting recommended minimum levels of activity; 70 per cent do not consume the recommended amount of fruit and vegetables; 26 per cent are obese; 21 per cent smoke; and 27 per cent of men and 18 per cent of women drink more than recommended safe limits of alcohol. Although reported levels of physical activity are rising and levels of smoking are declining slightly, rates of obesity are predicted to continue to rise. The rates are higher in more disadvantaged groups. These behaviours significantly increase the risk of chronic disease, including cancer, and reduce life expectancy.

There have been some improvements in lifestyle risks across the population; the greatest improvements are in higher socio-economic and educational groups

While professional groups have seen significant falls in the proportion with three or four unhealthy behaviours, there has been no significant fall for unskilled groups.

More than 60 per cent of the population have a negative or fatalistic attitude towards their own health, particularly in more disadvantaged groups

If current attitudes continue, rates of avoidable ill-health and health inequalities are likely to grow.

There are some improving trends in behaviour of young people, but many continue to have a poor diet

Rates of drinking, smoking and drug-taking in the young have fallen significantly over the past 10 years. Obesity rates in the young are also falling and levels of activity increasing, largely through increased activity at school. However, 80 per cent of children still have a poor diet and do not eat the recommended amounts of fruit and vegetables.

Key uncertainties

Behaviours and attitudes towards health

It is difficult to predict how people's attitude to their health and behaviour will change over time. Current trends suggest a growing socio-economic divide as those who are better off take on board health messages and adopt healthier lifestyles and those from more disadvantaged backgrounds do not. The improvements seen in young people's behaviour suggest that they may take a more positive approach to their health as they grow older.

Regulatory environment

The current Government has shown reluctance to regulate the food and drinks industry, but as pressures on health budgets grow this attitude may change and could have an impact on the nation's health.

Impact of unhealthy behaviours on the NHS and wider economy

Sources: *Department of Health Chief Medical Officer Annual Report 2009; **Estimates by The King's Fund based on Department of Health, Chief Medical Officer Annual Report 2009

⇨ The above information is reprinted with kind permission from The King's Fund. Please visit www.kingsfund.org.uk for further information.

© The King's Fund 2017

Diabetes patients who avoid annual health checks could double risk of early death

"We need to make sure the message gets through to everyone living with diabetes."

By Natasha Hinde

People who skip their annual diabetes checks could be doubling their risk of an early death, according to NHS Digital data.

Diabetes patients are now being urged to make sure they are having the potentially life-saving annual health checks.

In response to the report, Diabetes UK said more needs to be done to ensure people with the condition don't slip through the net.

The charity added that tackling diabetes must remain a top priority for the Government and healthcare providers.

A national diabetes audit looked at the link between three of the key annual diabetes health checks recommended by the National Institute for Health and Care Excellence (NICE) and mortality rates.

It found the risk of premature death for people with diabetes was more than twice as high for those who had not consistently had their blood glucose, cholesterol and blood pressure checked in the previous seven years.

The report also highlighted that the relative risk of death for people with diabetes is higher than for the general population, particularly in people of working age.

It also revealed that worryingly large numbers of people are still not getting all the checks they need.

For people with Type 1 diabetes, the risk of death was 127.8% higher than the wider population, while for those with Type 2 diabetes it was 28.4%.

Robin Hewings, head of policy at Diabetes UK, said: "Annual health checks and effective support for self-management mean some of the serious complications of diabetes can be avoided or treated early, enabling people with diabetes to live long, healthy lives.

"It is unacceptable that the risk of early death continues to be so much higher for people with diabetes, a condition that is costing the NHS more than £10 billion every year, the majority of which is spent on managing the devastating complications experienced by people with diabetes and their families."

People with diabetes are at increased risk of complications including kidney disease and cardiovascular problems, which are hugely expensive to treat.

The recommended annual health checks include measuring blood pressure, cholesterol and a kidney function test. By testing these, problems can be identified and treated before they become too serious.

"Complications such as heart attacks, stroke and kidney failure devastate families, and cost billions – yet still people are missing out," Hewings continued.

"Much more needs to be done to ensure people aren't slipping through the net and missing out on health checks that could literally save their lives.

"Tackling diabetes must remain a top priority for government and healthcare providers. Everyone with diabetes should have access to these tests no matter where they live, whatever their age or type of diabetes.

"It's essential that GPs continue to receive incentives to provide them and reach out to everyone that needs them – we need to make sure the message gets through to everyone living with diabetes."

13 July 2017

⇨ The above information is reprinted with kind permission from The Huffington Post UK. Please visit www.huffingtonpost.co.uk for further information.

More than 170,000 people are alive despite being diagnosed with cancer more than 25 years ago

New report from Macmillan Cancer Support celebrates advances in cancer treatment and care but warns more needs to be done to cope with increasing demand.

More than 170,000 people are living with cancer in the UK who were diagnosed in the 1970s and 1980s, according to new research released by Macmillan Cancer Support and Public Health England's National Cancer Registration and Analysis Service (NCRAS).

In a new report *Cancer: Then and Now* out today, Macmillan reveals for the first time the number of cancer survivors from the 1970s and 1980s in the UK. People on average are twice as likely to survive at least ten years after being diagnosed with cancer than they were at the start of the 1970s. These improvements in survival are partly due to earlier diagnosis – by way of screening programmes and advances in diagnostic tools, as well as more refined treatment.

The report compares the diagnosis, treatment and care of cancer then, to the experiences of cancer in the 2010s. While documenting drastic improvements over this time, particularly in available treatments, it also acts as a stark reminder that cancer continues to be a devastating diagnosis and one which affects a person long after their treatment has finished.

It highlights the consistent and growing support the charity offers people affected by cancer, including the introduction of Macmillan nurses in 1975 to the first Macmillan-trained benefits adviser in 2005. The charity, launches its brand new advertising campaign today which shows the breadth of services available to people affected by cancer such as Macmillan professionals, information and services and warns that demand for these services will continue to grow as more people with cancer live longer.

But those who survive many years after a cancer diagnosis do not necessarily have a good quality of life. Macmillan estimates that there could be around 42,500 people living with cancer who were diagnosed in the 1970s and 1980s who may still be dealing with problems linked to their cancer, such as long-term side effects.

Even today patients still need tailored support to manage the aftermath of cancer, as many may still have to deal with long-term side effects in the future. Around 625,000 people in the UK are estimated to be facing poor health or disability after treatment for cancer. Long-term side effects can include chronic fatigue, incontinence and sexual difficulties. That's why Macmillan offers patients a range of information guidance on late effects of treatment as well as specialist clinical services across the country.

With the numbers of people living with cancer in the UK set to grow from 2.5 million people to four million by 2030 more people than ever will need support with the long-term effect of cancer.

While the charity provides a range of information through its website, mobile units and information centres, it is vital that the NHS ensures patients are given all the right support and know where to find information and help when they need it. Worryingly, recent analysis from Macmillan shows

Estimated number of people living with cancer, at the end of 2010, 2015, 2020 and 2030

	2010	2015	2020	2030
England	1,700,000	2,000,000	2,400,000	3,400,000
Wales	110,000	130,000	160,000	220,000
Scotland	190,000	220,000	260,000	360,000
Northern Ireland	53,000	63,000	74,000	100,000
UK	2,100,000	2,500,000	2,900,000	4,000,000

Note: UK totals may not sum up due to rounding.

Number of older people (65 and over) living with a cancer diagnosis in the UK

2010 – 1,309,000

2040 – 4,109,000

= 100,00 people

Source: Macmillian Cancer Support

as money worries if they are too ill to work. In the future we will have even more people living with cancer in the long-term. Our health service needs to be equipped to meet the increasing demand over the coming years."

Lynda Thomas, Chief Executive at Macmillan Cancer Support, says:

"Today's report highlights the ever-changing story of cancer in this country. And today we launch our brand new advertising campaign which highlights the breadth of Macmillan services available today to help people not only cope with the devastating news that they have cancer, but the impact this has on their work, finances, relationships and of course, their health. We're still here, as we were decades ago, to reach as many people affected by this disease as we can – as the numbers rise and their needs get more complex."

1 August 2016

⇨ The above information is reprinted with kind permission from Macmillan. Please visit www.macmillan.org.uk for further information.

© Macmillan 2017

Online pharmacies not requiring prescriptions could fuel antibiotic resistance

By Caroline Brogan

Scientists have found that antibiotics are illegally available without prescription on 45 per cent of online pharmacy websites surveyed, says study.

The researchers from Imperial College London analysed 20 pharmacies that were available for UK citizens to access online. This is one of the few studies to have examined the online availability of antibiotics and to have explored the potential effects on public health. The research is published in *Journal of Antimicrobial Chemotherapy*.

Antibiotics are classed as prescription-only medicines in the UK, meaning they cannot legally be sold to consumers without a valid prescription. In this study, the researchers found that although online versions of UK high street pharmacies were compliant with prescription regulations, 80 per cent of the online pharmacies surveyed let customers choose their dosages, the duration and choice of antibiotic treatments. This can lead to serious side effects in patients and increases the risk of antimicrobial resistance.

Antimicrobial resistance is one of the biggest threats to global health, food security, and development today, according to the World Health Organization (WHO).

The team carried out their research entering the search term 'buy antibiotics online' into Google and Yahoo. They recognise that the study is a small 'snapshot' of the online

Antibiotics: dos and dont's
To the best of your knowledge, can the following conditions be cured by taking the right antibiotic?

	% GB Adults		
	YES	NO	DK
Bacterial infection	88	8	4
Ear infection	80	11	9
Kidney infection	77	11	13
Pneumonia	70	16	14
Viral infection	41	54	5
A regular sore throat	24	66	10
Flu	21	74	5
A cough	16	76	8
Common cold	8	87	5
Aches and pains	7	87	6
A hangover	2	92	6

7% have taken a course of antibiotics that wasn't prescribed by a doctor

Usually correct
Usually incorrect

18% have finished taking antibiotics before the end of the course, because they began to feel well

Source: GOVUK

pharmacy industry, but it does provide insights into how the industry operates. The 20 pharmacies at the top of the search were analysed by the team.

The study was carried out by academics from Imperial College London's NIHR Health Protection Research Unit for Healthcare Associated Infections and Antimicrobial Resistance, and Imperial College Healthcare NHS Trust.

Dr Sara Boyd, a co-author and NIHR Academic Clinical Fellow in Infectious Diseases and Microbiology at Imperial, said: "These findings are a real concern, and raise several important issues regarding antibiotic resistance and patient safety with online pharmacies."

All online medicine vendors selling to UK consumers must by law register with both the Medicines and Healthcare products Regulatory Agency (MHRA) and the General Pharmaceutical Council (or the Pharmaceutical Society of Northern Ireland). However, the researchers found that 75 per cent of online pharmacies included in the study lacked evidence of the appropriate registration status required by law.

In other findings, the researchers discovered that 45 per cent of the online pharmacies analysed did not require a prescription from the patient.

Only 30 per cent of websites in the survey asked consumers to complete a health questionnaire prior to purchase.

70 per cent of the websites provided information on the safe usage of prescription medications, including potential side effects or adverse reactions when combined with other drugs.

Professor Alison Holmes, of Imperial's Department of Medicine, added: "Improper use of antibiotics can mean that infections are not being treated appropriately, or that people are being unnecessarily exposed to antibiotics. This allows bacteria to become resistant to the drugs that once killed them. As a result, it is essential that antibiotics are prescribed only when they are needed."

Martin Astbury, President of the Royal Pharmaceutical Society, said: "Unnecessary antibiotic use can result in serious side effects in individuals

and has a major impact on wider public health by increasing antibiotic resistance. We cannot support access to antibiotics through a web form until the standards for prescribing by private providers reflect the standard of face to face consultations in the NHS. Those involved in supplying medicines online should ensure their processes are as robust as possible."

Shifts in patient behaviour

Although this is a small study, the authors say that the research offers insight into the increasing use of the Internet for a variety of purposes, including buying antibiotics. Dr Boyd said: "The way patients interact with healthcare is constantly evolving, and shifts in consumer behaviour mean more people are purchasing their goods online. Our study paves the way for larger, more thorough research into this worrying new trend so that we can ensure patient safety and promote the responsible use of antibiotics in all areas of healthcare provision."

All online pharmacies identified as illegally selling antibiotics to patients

within the UK were reported to the MHRA, who promptly responded. The researchers are working together with numerous stakeholders to improve patient safety and antibiotic responsibility in this area.

Anyone with concerns about an online pharmacy should contact the MHRA directly.

The study was partially funded by the National Institute for Health Research Health Protection Research Unit in Healthcare Associated Infections and Antimicrobial Resistance at Imperial College London, in partnership with Public Health England and Imperial College Healthcare NHS Trust.

17 February 2017

⇨ The above information is reprinted with kind permission from Imperial College London. Please visit www.imperial.ac.uk for further information.

The NHS faces a staffing crisis for years to come

An article from The Conversation.

THE CONVERSATION

By Elizabeth Rosser, Acting Dean of the Faculty of Health and Social Sciences, Bournemouth University

From August 2017, nursing, midwifery and most allied health students will no longer have their tuition fees paid by the NHS, nor will they receive maintenance bursaries. This will undoubtedly affect the number of students opting to study these subjects. And it will negatively impact NHS England staffing levels in three years' time.

Many nursing students are mature students and having their fees paid has been an incentive to study. At Bournemouth University, we have a large number of mature students who have a mortgage and dependent children, so they may be reluctant to take on more debt. Taking away the bursary could prevent many talented people from becoming tomorrow's nurses, midwives, physiotherapists, occupational therapists and speech-and-language therapists, to name just some of the healthcare degrees that will no longer be funded by the Government.

The Royal College of Nursing (RCN) confirms that nursing and midwifery student applications across England are down by 23% this year. This doesn't necessarily mean that the places on these courses won't be filled, as they are often oversubscribed, but it's a worrying dip, nonetheless.

If the Government – whoever they may be after June 8 – is serious about securing an NHS workforce for the future, they need to be serious about investing in it now.

Inventing new roles

There are over 55,000 EU nationals working as nurses and doctors in the NHS. As a result of Brexit, fewer nurses from the EU are applying for jobs in the NHS. And the RCN confirms that student nurse applications from EU citizens are down 7% this year.

New healthcare roles have been created in an attempt to counteract the changes to student funding and to Brexit, such as the new nursing associate role. A nursing associate is more junior than a registered nurse, but they can go on to become a registered nurse either by completing a degree-level nursing apprenticeship or by taking a shortened nursing degree at university.

The Government has also expanded the range of apprenticeship schemes, such as nursing-degree apprenticeships and apprenticeships which support the development of advanced-practice nurses. But none of these initiatives is a quick fix.

In fact, with the introduction of the apprenticeship levy, introduced for all large organisations since April 2017, the Government hopes to train 100,000 apprentices in the NHS by 2020. These apprenticeships will include nursing associates and healthcare assistants (a position below nursing associates). This means that all organisations, not just the NHS, who have an annual wage bill of £3m or more will have an apprenticeship levy of 0.5% of their total wage bill deducted to pay towards the government's apprenticeships scheme. However, paying for a three-year degree apprenticeship by the NHS Trusts will far exceed what the levy will pay for.

Dire consequences

Nursing shortages will not just be bad for patients, they will be bad for nurses too. A study, published in JAMA, showed that a poor nurse-to-patient ratio can result in an increase in patient mortality and have a detrimental effect on the health and wellbeing of the nurse, leading to job dissatisfaction and more nurses quitting.

The NHS cannot survive the continued and worsening workforce shortage and retain its reputation for high-quality patient care. So, unless incentives are introduced, such as fees paid for those with a first degree to enter these programmes at the postgraduate level, or assistance with childcare, or similar incentives that would encourage candidates to enter healthcare professions, the workforce crisis in the NHS can only continue to spiral out of control.

31 May 2017

⇨ The above information is reprinted with kind permission from *The Conversation*. Please visit www.theconversation.com for further information.

© 2010–2017, The ConversationTrust (UK)

Wraparound care: is it the future of the NHS?

As NHS chiefs push ahead with plans to transform local services, in Dorset controversial reforms mean more integration of health and social care – but also fewer hospital beds.

By Denis Campbell

"This is a way of working that's so obviously beneficial that I'm not sure why we didn't do it before. We've gone from uncoordinated, fragmented care that was very unsatisfactory for patients, to wraparound care that takes into account the holistic needs of the patient." Dr Karen Kirkham, a GP in Weymouth, is describing how Dorset has been quietly implementing a different way of providing healthcare which, if it works out, might just help save the NHS.

Sitting in a side room at Weymouth's Westhaven community hospital, Kirkham outlines an approach that is simultaneously radical and commonsensical, and also controversial, despite being backed by all those whose job is to improve the health of Dorset's 750,000 residents. "In Dorset, necessity has been the mother of invention. We've taken the issue of relentlessly rising demand and proposed bold action to adapt what we do for our patients," she adds. While all this sounds novel, it is also one of the oldest tunes in the jukebox of NHS great policy ideas.

By bold action she means integration – both of health services and also health services with social care – reconfiguration of acute hospital services and the creation of ten "hubs" to coordinate or deliver a recently extended array of out-of-hospital services. Dorset's push to modernise how health and social care work is so advanced that on Friday NHS England's chief executive, Simon Stevens, will name it as one of the official microcosms of the "new NHS" he has pledged to create by 2020.

Dorset will be one of between six and ten areas of England in which Stevens will give the green light to the local NHS sustainability and transformation plan (STP). These will be the first wave of what he still hopes will ultimately be all 44 regional STPs, each doing their bit to implement the "five-year forward view" he originally set out in October 2014. Its mission: to make the NHS sustainable as a system of healthcare by both improving quality of care and preventing illness occurring in the first place, while simultaneously somehow bridging the £22 billion gap in the service's finances expected by 2020. Stevens's "delivery plan" this week will hail Dorset as a pioneer from whom the wider NHS can learn a lot.

Kirkham has played a key role in recent years in building agreement between Dorset's three acute NHS trusts, one community services trust, 97 GP practices, three local councils and 30,000 clinical staff – and Dorset NHS clinical commissioning group (CCG), with which she is the assistant clinical chair – that working together is the right direction of travel. NHS and town hall chiefs across the country recognised in 2015 that they had to transform how they provided health and social care if services were, in her words, to avoid being "overwhelmed with demand" caused by the ageing population.

Dorset CCG's Your NHS document, which explains what it admits are "large-scale changes to health and care services in both community and hospital settings", is admirably no-nonsense on the urgent need for change. "Doing nothing is not an option, because by staying the same our healthcare would get much worse. Doing nothing would mean lower safety standards, worsening health [and] reduced survival rates," it says.

Integrated community services are a key element of the STP's ambition to keep people out of hospital, provide much more care in or near people's homes and ensure that the anticipated £229 million deficit in Dorset's NHS finances does not emerge as expected by 2021. And the ten "community hubs" are the key to making integration itself work. They are all similar in that they all coordinate the delivery of care; but while seven have beds attached for patients, three do not.

The hub for Weymouth is no more than a room at Westhaven hospital full of desks, computers and telephones. But this is where different types of care professionals – including GPs and personnel from the ambulance service, local acute hospital, social care and district nursing services – work together to take calls from fellow professionals, discuss individual patients' needs and decide how each is cared for.

"It's a simple idea – that when GPs need to refer a patient, for surgery or a home visit or a residential home placement, they ring one number and refer the problem to the team in the hub, and they decide what to do. It's a one-stop shop," explains Dr Riaz Dharamshi, a consultant geriatrician who works two-and-a-half days a week with the hub team, including paying home visits to frail, elderly people.

Louise Clark, head of occupational therapy at Dorset healthcare NHS foundation trust, explains: "If we need to discharge someone from the local acute hospital we refer them to the hub. They arrange the care that someone needs – therapy, district nurses or mental health input, so that the person can go home safely. They wrap the care around them in a way that didn't happen before."

The service is aimed primarily at frail elderly people, who comprise about 80% of all hospital inpatients these days and are therefore a huge driver of the increasing costs facing the NHS as a whole. Dorset's coastline and quality of life means it has far more over-75s and more over-85s than the average for England, with those numbers due to swell in coming years.

If one of them needs an investigation, or rehabilitation after a spell in hospital, then they go into Westhaven's 34-bed ward. "That might be someone who has become confused or had a fall but not broken a bone," says Dharamshi. The average age of those admitted here is 86.

A similarly joined-up, multidisciplinary approach elsewhere in Dorset, coupled with the opening last September of a frailty unit at Royal Bournemouth hospital, has seen the average length of stay for acutely frail elderly people treated in its older people's medicine wards fall from 10.3 days as recently as April 2016 to just 5.87 days now – a difference of 4.43 days. As it costs £400 a night to keep a patient in an acute hospital, that means the average cost of treating a patient has fallen from £4,120 to £1,772.

Dr Andrew Williams, the hospital's clinical director of older people's medicine, stresses that the motivation for everyone working together to support medically vulnerable older people is not financial. "The project was about improving patient outcomes, not cash savings," he says. Stopping older people becoming inpatients unnecessarily means they are much less likely to get "deconditioned" – to lose vital muscle mass due to being in hospital – which makes them more likely to fall over, lose their independence and have further complications, he adds.

There are other big benefits, too. Extra care at home means the average length of time for which such patients need support after discharge has fallen from 32 to 24 days. And this means the hospital has more spare beds, is more likely to hit its four-hour A&E target and less likely to have to cancel operations due to overcrowding.

Other elements of Dorset's STP are certainly proving controversial: Bournemouth becomes the main acute hospital, while Poole will play the lead role for non-urgent care. As a result, Poole is set to lose its A&E unit and maternity and paediatric services. In all, 100 acute beds are due to go across the county, at least three community hospitals face the axe, while the number of beds in the remaining community hospitals will also be dramatically scaled back. Poole residents and campaign groups 38 Degrees and the NHS Support Federation are among those that have voiced concern.

But Stevens sees Dorset as a trailblazer, a crucible of how the entire NHS across England needs to work. "Dorset's NHS has been ahead of the game in spotting that the local NHS needs to join forces to be more than the sum of its parts. They are proposing important changes for patients.

"It has been clear for a long time that the traditional divide between GPs, hospitals and community services is increasingly a barrier to the personalised, coordinated healthcare patients need. We can see in Dorset that this is the kind of practical improvement that many doctors, nurses and carers are now beginning to create."

29 March 2017

⇨ The above information is reprinted with kind permission from *The Guardian*. Please visit www.theguardian.com for further information.

How AI could provide respite to NHS crisis

An article from The Conversation.

THE CONVERSATION

By Emma Rich, University of Bath and Andy Miah, University of Salford

The NHS recently announced plans to trial an artificially intelligent mobile health app to a million people in London. The aim is to help diagnose and treat patients by engaging them in a real time text message conversation which will complement the NHS 111 phone based service (which was criticised by the Care Quality Commission watchdog). The app's designers, Babylon Healthcare Ltd, use algorithms to make initial diagnoses which are then followed up with human consultations. It has already received a glowing CQC evaluation.

The app is likely to provoke a mixed response, with enthusiastic technophiles up against those concerned that more technology means a less human healthcare service. Yet, with the NHS being described as suffering from a humanitarian crisis, and with a growing healthcare burden and limited resources, some smart solutions are needed. It is hard to deny that problems of limited funding are enduring features of this unique public service. Perhaps AI has the answer.

In fact, providing effective healthcare is always a combination of systematised technological efficiency combined with patient centred human care. Polarised views on technology are often not helpful. It's also necessary to recognise how this approach to healthcare is part of a wider technical revolution in which connected objects in the Internet of Things will change everything from healthcare to traffic maintenance.

The NHS app is really simple to use and has been likened to using the social messaging service WhatsApp – but with one crucial difference: you are chatting with a computer, not a person. Once the app is downloaded, you log your basic health information, and then start explaining your symptoms. The robotic "responder" will say things like: "I just need a few details from you before we get started," and "nearly there" to keep the conversation going. After a more detailed exchange, it might come to a conclusion along these lines:

"OK so your symptoms don't sound urgent, but I think they require further investigation. Make sure you arrange a consultation with a GP within the next two weeks. If left, symptoms like yours can become more serious, so book now while you remember and I'll remind you closer to the time. If things change in the meantime and you become more unwell, speak to a doctor as soon as you can."

This digital diagnosis service intends to provide an additional communication tool between the NHS and patients. It it part of a broader ecosystem of digital health services which include online health tracking. Also, the app takes advantage of the fact that some people these days are likely to be more comfortable chatting by text than they are with talking on the phone.

This digital phenomenon is driven by the promise of a wider technological fix to social problems. Applications

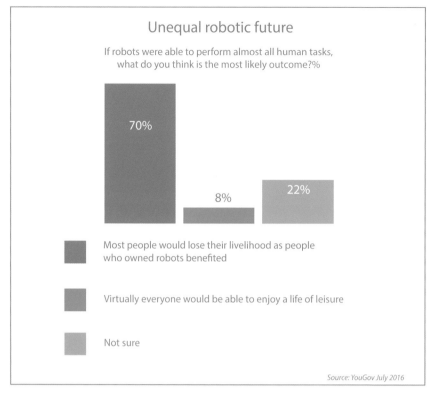

Unequal robotic future

If robots were able to perform almost all human tasks,
what do you think is the most likely outcome?%

70%

8%

22%

■ Most people would lose their livelihood as people
who owned robots benefited

■ Virtually everyone would be able to enjoy a life of leisure

■ Not sure

Source: YouGov July 2016

within healthcare could bring about big wins for society, where the functionality of the device is made all the more efficient by the aggregation of 'big data' that it generates. Tech firm Babylon is joined by other big players seeking to do similar things, such as Google's Deep Mind, which wants to mine NHS data to to enable earlier diagnoses for example, or to achieve more effective monitoring of treatments.

At the world's largest tech expo in Las Vegas at the start of 2017, home AI systems have been one of the biggest hits. So perhaps the NHS has found an intelligent solution at just the right time. People may now be far more willing to have a 'relationship' with an attentive machine than a call centre drone.

Digital doctor

Driving these developments is the assumption that, within a digital knowledge economy, these forms of communication can offer more neutral and accurate responses, circumventing human error. Yet, scholars within the emerging field of critical digital health studies suggest that algorithms must be understood as part of a complex network of interconnections between human and non-human actors. A recent study comparing physician and computer diagnostic

accuracy revealed that doctors "vastly outperformed" algorithms.

So we need to ask some key questions about the assimilation of AI into healthcare. How do people make sense of the list of possible diagnoses they receive from the machine? Will people follow the advice, or trust it? How will AI need to be tailored to accommodate

human variation, by geography, capacity, or cultural identity. Another important aspect of this trial will be the consideration given to the backgrounds of the users. Given enduring concerns about inequalities of digital access and digital literacy, trials for future digital health tech need to be conducted amongst those populations with limited resources, experiences and technological infrastructure.

Perhaps the biggest question we face in a world where ever more of our data is locked up in the mobile app environment, is over the proprietary and privacy of our data. How can we ensure that we have the freedom to move our health data around, over time, and ensure that it is safe and secure? We may need a new Bill of Health Data Rights to underpin and limit their exploitation of our data, and work on this must start now.

13 January 2017

⇨ The above information is reprinted with kind permission from *The Conversation*. Please visit www. theconversation.com for further information.

© 2010–2017,
The Conversation Trust (UK)

Five ways virtual reality is improving healthcare

An article from The Conversation.

By Wendy Powell, Reader in Virtual Reality, University of Portsmouth

Virtual reality is much more than just a new form of entertainment, it is increasingly being used in a wide range of medical applications, from treatments to training. Here are a few of them.

1. Pain management

There is good scientific evidence that virtual reality (VR) can help relieve pain. The parts of the brain that are linked to pain – the somatosensory cortex and the insula – are less active when a patient is immersed in virtual reality. In some instances, it can even help people tolerate medical procedures that are usually very painful.

Other studies have shown that amputees can benefit from VR therapy. Amputees often feel severe pain in their missing limb, which can be hard to treat with conventional methods, and often doesn't respond well to strong painkillers like codeine and morphine. However, a technique called 'virtual mirror therapy', which involves putting on a VR headset and controlling a virtual version of the absent limb seems to help some patients cope better with this 'phantom pain'.

2. Physical therapy

VR can be used to track body movements, allowing patients to use the movements of their therapy exercises as interactions in a VR game. For example, they may need to lift an arm above their head in order to catch a virtual ball.

It's more fun doing exercises in virtual reality than it is in a gym, so people are more motivated to exercise. It can help in other ways too. For example, we found that for patients who are anxious about walking, we can control their virtual environment so that it looks as though they are moving much slower than they actually are. When we do this, they naturally speed up their walking, but they don't realise they are doing it and so it isn't associated with pain or anxiety.

Studying how people perceive and interact with VR systems helps us design better rehabilitation applications.

3. Fears and phobias

If you have an irrational fear of something, you might think the last thing you need is to see it in virtual reality, however, this is one of most established forms of medical VR treatment. Phobias are often treated with something called graded-exposure therapy, where patients are slowly introduced to their fear by a therapist. Virtual reality is perfect for this as it can be adjusted precisely for the needs of each patient, and can be done in the doctor's office or even at home. This is being used to treat phobias such as fear of heights and fear of spiders, but also to help people recover from post-traumatic stress disorder (PTSD).

4. Cognitive rehabilitation

Patients with brain injury from trauma or illness, such as stroke, often struggle with the everyday tasks that we take for granted, such as shopping or making plans for the weekend. Recreating these tasks within virtual environments and allowing patients to practise them at increasing levels of complexity can speed up recovery and help patients regain a higher level of cognitive function.

Doctors can also use these same virtual environments as an assessment tool, observing patients carrying out a variety of real-world complex tasks and identifying areas of memory loss, reduced attention or difficulty with decision-making.

5. Training doctors and nurses

Virtual reality is, of course, not just for patients. It also offers benefits to healthcare professionals. Training doctors and nurses to carry out routine procedures is time consuming, and training generally needs to be delivered by a busy – and expensive – professional. But virtual reality is increasingly being used to learn anatomy, practise operations and teach infection control.

Being immersed in a realistic simulation of a procedure and practising the steps and techniques is far better training than watching a video, or even standing in a crowded room watching an expert. With low-cost VR equipment, controllable, repeatable scenarios and instant feedback, we have a powerful new teaching tool that reaches well beyond the classroom.

20 January 2017

⇨ The above information is reprinted with kind permission from *The Conversation*. Please visit www.theconversation.com for further information.

Medical advances

This article reviews some of the key areas for medical advances over the next 20 years, including pharmaceutical and surgical innovation and regenerative medicine.

Key messages

Pharmaceutical innovation could provide new treatment for common diseases

Innovation in drug discovery, genetics, biotechnology, material sciences and bioinformatics has already improved treatments for conditions such as HIV, cancer and heart disease and offers hope of better treatments for neurodegenerative diseases.

Advances in diagnostics, devices and robotics could improve outcomes

Developments in diagnostics and drug delivery could reduce drug errors, increase compliance and improve efficacy.

Precision medicine could revolutionise our ability to predict, prevent and treat a range of conditions

Low-cost genetic sequencing, genome mapping, biomarker tests, and targeted drugs and treatments will enable professionals to provide tailored health information and create personalised treatments to improve patient outcomes.

Regenerative medicine shows potential but wide-scale benefits remain elusive

Despite advances in stem cell transplantation, cell reprogramming and synthetic and artificial organs, effective and safe regenerative therapies remain elusive and expensive and have yet to be realised on a wide scale.

Technological advances could transform interactions between professionals and patients

Professionals can already hold consultations with, monitor and deliver care to patients at home using home-based remote technologies and video conferencing. This trend is likely

to continue. In the future, medical 'apps' for mobile phones will also allow patients to access their medical records, make appointments and seek personalised health information and support.

Budget constraints may limit the ability of the NHS to support and benefit from medical innovation

There is a real risk that medical advances could fuel demand for care. Innovations can extend the range of patients eligible for treatment, and so increase overall activity.

Key uncertainties

Uncertainties about the nature and speed of medical advances could impact on the trends in health and social care. For example, in the past forecasts have been over-optimistic about xeno-transplantation and gene therapy, while underestimating the speed and impact of breakthroughs in CT scanning and minimally invasive surgery.

Interplay between technology, evidence and affordability

Budgetary constraints could act as a major barrier in the adoption of new medical technologies. However, a more evidence-based approach

targeting resources at interventions which have the greatest benefit could release resources for investment elsewhere.

Rate of adoption

Rates of adoption of new medical technologies can be highly variable. Uptake can be particularly slow if it requires a new pathway of care to support it, such as in telecare.

Technological interdependencies

Biomarkers may have the potential to enable clinicians to diagnose and treat conditions much more effectively, tailoring therapies to the individual. However, this technology is heavily reliant upon advances in other fields, including molecular biology and genomics. This type of interdependency could affect the rate at which developments move into clinical use.

Date?

⇨ The above information is reprinted with kind permission from The King's Fund. Please visit www.kingsfund.org.uk for further information.

Key facts

- The NHS in England deals with over one million patients every 36 hours. It covers everything, including antenatal screening, routine screenings (such as the NHS Health Check), treatments for long-term conditions, transplants, emergency treatment and end-of-life care. (page 1)

- The NHS employs more than 1.5 million people, putting it in the top five of the world's largest workforces, together with the US Department of Defence, McDonalds, Walmart and the Chinese People's Liberation Army. (page 1)

- The NHS in Scotland, Wales and Northern Ireland employs 161,415, 84,000 and 66,000 people, respectively. (page 1)

- In France, all health transactions centre on a smartcard, the Carte Vitale. A GP visit costs €23 (£17), the Carte Vitale is swiped and the money is paid back into the patient's bank account within five days. In general, the state reimbursement rate is between 70% and 100%. The poorest people and the long-term sick are covered 100%. (page 4)

- In Ireland, most individuals pay for prescriptions from pharmacies capped at €144 per month under the Drugs Payment Scheme. Medical cardholders do not pay for medication but do pay a prescription charge of €2.50 per item (capped at €25 per month per person/family). (page 4)

- Japan spends a sharply rising proportion of GDP on healthcare but falls down on the amount of time people spend in hospital, which is one of the highest among rich countries. (page 5)

- In 2011–12, 57% of adult Australians had private health insurance, particularly older people, high earners and women in their 20s and 30s who use it for maternity care. (page 7)

- The Government plans to spend around £122 billion on health in England in 2017/18, or roughly £2,200 per person. Around £108 billion will be spent on the day-to-day running of the NHS. (page 10)

- Health spending in Northern Ireland in 2016/17 was £5 billion, or roughly £2,700 per person. (page 10)

- Total health spending in England was nearly £124 billion in 2017/18 and is expected to rise to over £125 billion by 2020, taking inflation into account. (page 11)

- The NHS England budget is expected to rise by about £9 billion from 2015/16 to 2020/21, taking inflation into account. Meanwhile spending on the other areas is set to fall by £3.1 billion. (page 12)

- In 2015, 16% were dissatisfied with GPs. Despite media attention over the past few years reporting pressures in general practice, levels of dissatisfaction in 2015 are similar to those seen a decade earlier. However, there is a small but significant upward trend over the last few years with dissatisfaction rising from 12% in 2009 to 16% in 2015. (page 16)

- There were 501,424 deaths registered in 2014, this represents a decrease of 5,366 deaths compared with 2013, a fall of 1.1%. (page 23)

- Heart diseases were the leading cause of death for men in 2014 (14.8% of male deaths), while for women it was dementia and Alzheimer disease (13.4% of female deaths). (page 23)

- In 2014, 871 boys and 542 girls died aged five to 19. Suicide, including injury or poisoning of undetermined intent, combined with land transport accidents, accounted for one in four deaths among males and one in five deaths among females in this age group in 2014. (page 24)

- Air pollution is linked to an estimated 40,000 early deaths a year and 37 out of 43 areas across the UK are exceeding legal European Union limits for key pollutant nitrogen dioxide, much of which comes from diesel engines. (page 26)

- 66 per cent of the adult population are not meeting recommended minimum levels of activity; 70 per cent do not consume the recommended amount of fruit and vegetables; 26 per cent are obese; 21 per cent smoke; and 27 per cent of men and 18 per cent of women drink more than recommended safe limits of alcohol. (page 29)

- More than 170,000 people are living with cancer in the UK who were diagnosed in the 1970s and 1980s, according to new research released by Macmillan Cancer Support and Public Health England's National Cancer Registration and Analysis Service (NCRAS). (page 31)

- Only 30 per cent of online pharmacy websites in a recent survey asked consumers to complete a health questionnaire prior to purchase. (page 33)

- There are over 55,000 EU nationals working as nurses and doctors in the NHS. As a result of Brexit, fewer nurses from the EU are applying for jobs in the NHS. And the RCN confirms that student nurse applications from EU citizens are down 7% this year. (page 35)

A&E

The Accident and Emergency department in an NHS hospital provides emergency medical care.

Antibiotic resistance

When an antibiotic has been used a lot, it can lose its ability to kill bacteria – the bacteria become 'resistant' to it.

Care Quality Commission

A body of the Department of Health, established to regulate and inspect health and social services in England.

Diabetes

A disease in which the body's ability to produce or respond to insulin in impaired.

Friends and Family Test

From April 2013, all patients treated in NHS wards or A&E departments will be asked on leaving whether they would recommend that department to their friends and family. The Government hope that this measure will help them to gauge the standard of treatment in NHS hospitals and also help people make decisions about where they want their medical care to be provided. Results are available on the NHS website.

Health and Social Care Act 2012

The biggest change to the NHS since it was very first started. Came into force in April 2013.

Health insurance/private medical insurance

Although UK citizens are entitled to free care via the NHS, many opt to pay into a private medical insurance policy so that they can choose where they are treated and receive a higher standard of care in more luxurious surroundings.

Health tourism

Foreign visitors who come to the UK so that they can claim free medical treatment that might not be available in their own country.

National Insurance

Taxes paid by employees and employers.

NHS

The National Health Service provides free medical care to citizens of England, Scotland, Wales and Northern Ireland.

NHS Direct

24 hour medical advice, provided by the NHS, available online and via telephone service.

Virtual reality

A 3D computer generated simulation that can be interacted with.

Assignments

Brainstorming

⇨ Brainstorm what you know about the NHS and health in the UK.

- What is the NHS?

- What kind of problems is the NHS facing at the moment?

- What do you think is the biggest health issue for people?

Research

⇨ Do some research about healthcare in the UK compared to other countries in the World. Choose one of the countries you come across and write a bullet point list of the similarities between that country and the UK.

⇨ Talk to friends and relatives about their experience of the NHS. Think of six questions to ask them and then write a report no longer than one page long.

⇨ Do some research into staffing shortages in the NHS. Write an article about how these shortages could be tackled.

⇨ Research Macmillan cancer care and write an article about their services.

⇨ In pairs, research loneliness in the UK's elderly population. How does loneliness lead to health problems? Share your findings with your class.

⇨ According to the article on page 29, 66 per cent of the adult population are not meeting the recommended levels of activity. Conduct a survey amongst your year group to find out how much activity people do on a daily basis. When you've gathered your results, write a short report and include at least two graphs.

Design

⇨ Choose an article from the book and design a poster which highlights the key themes of the piece.

⇨ Design a poster which would encourage people to apply for jobs in the NHS.

⇨ There are many services offered by the NHS. Create a leaflet informing people of the services available.

⇨ Design a children's hospital ward. Think about making it a safe, fun place for children to be.

⇨ Design an illustration to highlight the key themes/messages of the article on page 25.

⇨ Make an infographic from the graph which is shown on page 32.

Oral

⇨ Hold a class discussion about the crisis in the NHS, discuss staff shortages, underfunding and how overstretched the NHS is. Discuss ways you think these issues could be addressed.

⇨ Choose one of the illustrations from this book and, in pairs, discuss what you think the artist was trying to portray with their image. Would you change the illustration in any way?

⇨ In small groups, prepare a PowerPoint presentation that explains the signs and symptoms of air pollution. Share your findings with your class.

⇨ In pairs stage a discussion between two work colleagues where one of you is trying to persuade the other to cycle to work. Take it in turns to play the role of the persuader.

⇨ As a class look at the article on page 23 and the graph shown, discuss the main causes of death in the UK and give your views on what could be done to reduce the number of deaths.

⇨ In small groups discuss how virtual reality is improving healthcare. Consider the following:

- how can it improve tolerance to pain?

- how can it help to overcome phobias?

- how it is used to train doctors and nurses

Reading/writing

⇨ Write a one-paragraph definition of Diabetes

⇨ Read the article on page 30 relating to Diabetes and write a blog explaining why you think it is important to have regular check-ups.

⇨ 'The NHS is in crisis'. Write an essay exploring this statement. You should write at least two sides of A4.

⇨ A new report from Macmillan Cancer Support celebrates advances in cancer treatment and care but warns more needs to be done to cope with increasing demand. Write an article exploring recent advances which have been made.

⇨ Choose an article and write a one-page summary.

⇨ Read the article on page 36 and write down your thoughts regarding the use of such technology in diagnosing illness. Consider the following:

- Can we trust digital diagnosis to be accurate?

- What about patient's privacy?

Acknowledgements

The publisher is grateful for permission to reproduce the material in this book. While every care has been taken to trace and acknowledge copyright, the publisher tenders its apology for any accidental infringement or where copyright has proved untraceable. The publisher would be pleased to come to a suitable arrangement in any such case with the rightful owner.

Images

All images courtesy of iStock except page 28 © JD Mason, page 30 © Sonia Langford and page 38 © Scott Webb.

Icons

Icons on pages 21 and 31 were made by Freepik from www.flaticon.com.

Illustrations

Don Hatcher: pages 6 & 20. Simon Kneebone: pages 10 & 37. Angelo Madrid: pages 25 & 29.

Additional acknowledgements

Editorial on behalf of Independence Educational Publishers by Cara Acred.

With thanks to the Independence team: Shelley Baldry, Tina Brand, Sandra Dennis, Jackie Staines and Jan Sunderland.

Cara Acred

Cambridge, September 2017